ANSWER KEY

TESTS
for use with

Elements of
LITERATURE
for Christian Schools®

BJU PRESS

Greenville, South Carolina 29614 • www.bjup.com

182832

9 781579 246389

To the Teacher

For each of the eleven units of *ELEMENTS OF LITERATURE for Christian Schools,* we offer one test. We also include a comprehensive midterm examination over Units 1-6 and a comprehensive final examination over Units 7-11.

These tests are designed to help you evaluate your students' progress toward the stated objectives of the course. We realize that every teaching situation is different. You as the teacher should feel free to add, delete, or change any test item in order to create an instrument more suited to your own testing needs.

Multiple Choice

Choose the best answer from the choices given.

<u>**B**</u>
p. 5
1. Name the sense to which the following sensory image from "Dawn in the Forest" appeals most: "Beaded dewdrops stood upon the leaves and grasses."

   A. smell
   B. sight
   C. hearing
   D. touch

<u>**B**</u>
p. 5
2. Identify the imaginative comparison Twain uses in the following sentence from "Dawn in the Forest": "The marvel of Nature shaking off sleep and going to work unfolded itself to the musing boy."

   A. simile
   B. personification
   C. metonymy
   D. synecdoche

<u>**A**</u>
pp. 5-6
3. The only sight or sound that the author does *not* associate with dawn in the forest is

   A. the bluejay's dropping of the acorns.
   B. a ladybug climbing a grass blade.
   C. the trilling of a catbird.
   D. the hammering of a woodpecker.

<u>**A**</u>
p. 6
4. Identify the imaginative comparison Twain uses in the following sentence from "Dawn in the Forest": "He sat as still as a stone."

   A. simile
   B. personification
   C. metonymy
   D. synecdoche

<u>**B**</u>
p. 7
5. The most obvious imaginative comparisons in "What Stumped the Bluejays" are examples of

   A. metaphor.
   B. personification.
   C. simile.
   D. metonymy.

<u>**A**</u>
p. 8
6. What initially puzzles the bluejay when he begins dropping acorns in the hole?

   A. He cannot hear them hit the bottom of the hole.
   B. He does not understand why a roof would have a hole in it.
   C. He does not understand why other bluejays had not found such a perfect hole.
   D. The hole seems to be filling up quickly.

<u>**B**</u>
pp. 9-10
7. The mystery of the knothole is finally solved when

   A. one of the bluejays sees down the hole and explains what has happened.
   B. one of the bluejays looks in through the half-open door.
   C. one of the bluejays opens the door and looks in.
   D. a bluejay who already knows about the hole arrives at the scene.

__B__
p. 12

8. In "A Bird Came Down the Walk," what imaginative comparison is Dickinson using in her statement that the bird's eyes "looked like frightened Beads"?

   A. metonymy
   B. simile
   C. metaphor
   D. personification

__B__
p. 12

9. Identify the object or objects to which the bird's feathers are being compared in the following line from "A Bird Came Down the Walk": "And he unrolled his feathers."

   A. a ship's oars
   B. a ship's sails
   C. a ship's compass
   D. a ship's rudder

__D__
pp. 12-13

10. What imaginative comparison(s) does the poet use in both "A Bird Came Down the Walk" and "A Prompt, Executive Bird"?

   A. simile
   B. metaphor
   C. personification
   D. all of the above

__C__
TE p. 13

11. A play on words that are identical or similar in sound but different in meaning is a

   A. simile.
   B. metaphor.
   C. pun.
   D. homonym.

__A__
pp. 4, 13

12. The only one of the following lines from "A Prompt, Executive Bird" that does not contain a simile is

   A. "Brittle and brief in quality."
   B. "Bold as a Bailiff's hymn."
   C. "Sitting a bough like a Brigadier."
   D. "As a Magistrate."

__C__
p. 15

13. Which is the thesis sentence of Ruskin's "The Fly"?

   A. "You cannot terrify him."
   B. "He has no work to do, no tyrannical instinct to obey."
   C. "We can nowhere find a better type of perfectly free creature than in the common housefly."
   D. "All these are comparatively slaves, or people of business."

__B__
p. 15

14. In his description of the fly, Ruskin focuses primarily on the fly's

   A. arrogance.
   B. independence.
   C. beauty.
   D. relationship to man.

___C___ 15. Ruskin states that the fly exhibits all of the following traits *except*
p. 15

    A. egotism.
    B. self-confidence.
    C. fear.
    D. independence.

___A___ 16. Ruskin makes a comparison between the slapping motion of a man's hand and the
p. 15

    A. crashing down of an acre of red clay.
    B. mechanical marching of the fly.
    C. resolute observing of the fly.
    D. flitting and flirting of the fly.

___D___ 17. Ruskin pictures the fly's reaction to the slap of a man's hand as one of
p. 15

    A. terror.
    B. delight.
    C. anger.
    D. impudence.

___C___ 18. Identify the kind of imaginative comparison Ruskin uses in the following description of
p. 15   the fly: "He has his own positive opinion on all matters."

    A. simile
    B. metonymy
    C. personification
    D. synecdoche

___A___ 19. The fly's tendency to indulge in the sweets "in the grocer's window" as well as "those of
p. 15   the butcher's back yard" best illustrates the principle that

    A. unlimited freedom eventually results in a loss of the ability to discriminate properly.
    B. wonderful opportunities exist for those with unlimited freedom.
    C. one should seek as his goal the attainment of unlimited freedom.
    D. everyone has the right to enjoy unlimited freedom.

___B___ 20. The vehicle of comparison that Whitman introduces in the first stanza of "A Noiseless
p. 17   Patient Spider" is the

    A. spider standing isolated in the very center of its web.
    B. spider beginning to spin its web.
    C. soul standing detached in oceans of space.
    D. soul searching for the truth.

___C___ 21. In the second stanza, Whitman compares the first stanza's vehicle of comparison to
p. 17

    A. the formation of a bridge.
    B. gossamer threads.
    C. the soul's search for connection and foundation.
    D. a ductile anchor.

___A___ 22. The "soul" in Whitman's poem represents
p. 17,
TE p. 18
    A. men who are ceaselessly seeking for the truth.
    B. men who have reached the realization that they will never find the truth.
    C. men who at last have found the truth.
    D. men who are content without searching for the truth.

<u>**B**</u>
p. 19

23. According to "The Spider and the Wasp," the most important requirement in the struggle for survival for all species of animals is

   A. a place of habitation.
   B. an adequate source of food.
   C. protection from enemies.
   D. intelligence.

<u>**A**</u>
p. 19,
TE p. 23

24. Which sentence is the thesis sentence of "The Spider and the Wasp"?

   A. "In the feeding and safeguarding of their progeny the insects and spiders exhibit some interesting analogies to reasoning and some crass examples of blind instinct."
   B. "In a Paris museum is a tropical specimen which is said to have been in captivity for 25 years."
   C. "But all spiders, and especially hairy ones, have an extremely delicate sense of touch."
   D. "In a way the instinctive urge to escape is not only easier but more efficient than reasoning."

<u>**C**</u>
p. 20

25. When an object touches the body hair of a tarantula when the tarantula is not hungry, the spider responds by

   A. attacking the object.
   B. ignoring the object.
   C. shaking the touched limb.
   D. moving slowly away.

<u>**B**</u>
p. 21

26. Which statement does *not* apply to the digger wasps of the genus *Pepsis?*

   A. When they are ready to attack, they give off a pungent odor.
   B. Their sting is not as severe as that of a bee or common wasp.
   C. Their food source is nectar.
   D. The largest ones have almost a four-inch wingspan.

<u>**D**</u>
p. 22

27. During the battle between the digger wasp and the tarantula, all the following events take place *except*

   A. the wasp crawls around on the tarantula to determine its species.
   B. the wasp digs a grave for the tarantula.
   C. the wasp places her stinger into the joint where the tarantula's leg is joined to its body and injects a poison.
   D. the tarantula dies immediately as a result of the poison.

<u>**C**</u>
pp. 22-23

28. What does Petrunkevitch consider the most probable cause for the tarantula's "stupidity" in its encounter with the digger wasp?

   A. It recognizes that the digger wasp is much more powerful and so does not attempt to protect itself.
   B. It does not react to its own instincts.
   C. It follows its instinctive pattern of trying to escape rather than trying to defend itself.
   D. Its sensory organs are untrustworthy.

TEST 1

Short Answer

Write the word or phrase that best answers the question or defines the term.

29. To what does the term *metonymy* refer? *an expression in which a related thing stands for the thing itself, p. 4*

30. What is synecdoche? *an expression in which a part stands for the whole, p. 4*

31. "Dawn in the Forest" is an excerpt from what novel? *Tom Sawyer, p. 5*

32. In "Dawn in the Forest," with what creature five times larger than itself does Tom notice an ant struggling? *a spider, p. 6*

33. According to Tom, what insect is "credulous about conflagrations"? *the ladybug, p. 6*

34. In "A Bird Came Down the Walk," what "fellow" does the bird eat raw? *the angleworm, p. 12*

35. By what gesture does the poet offer the bird friendship? *the offer of a crumb, p. 12*

36. What two comparisons does the poet use to describe the bird's flight? *to ships and to butterflies, pp. 12-13*

37. What are the "Banks of Noon" from which the butterflies leap? *banks of flowers, p. 13*

38. What kind of bird does the poet describe in "A Prompt, Executive Bird"? *a blue jay, p. 13*

39. What three professions does Dickinson associate with the "Prompt, Executive Bird"? *bailiff, brigadier, magistrate, p. 13*

40. "The Spider and the Wasp" mentions trichobothria. What are trichobothria? *fine hairs that grow from disklike membranes on the tarantula's legs, p. 21*

41. According to Petrunkevitch's essay, which acts like the more intelligent animal, the spider or the wasp? *the wasp, p. 22*

True/False

If the statement is completely true, write *true*. If any part of the statement is false, write *false*.

true — 42. The Bible contains both poetry and prose.
p. x

true — 43. In both "Dawn in the Forest" and "A Bird Came Down the Walk," the authors make a
pp. 5-6,   seemingly trivial incident appear significant.
12-13

false — 44. Mark Twain was a devout believer in God's providence.
p. 11

true   45. The poet's use of "Banks of Noon" is a pun.
p. 13

true   46. Dickinson viewed the Bible as a source of poetic inspiration rather than as an inerrant
p. 14   guide to life.

false   47. Whitman uses a definite meter and rhyme scheme in "A Noiseless Patient Spider."
p. 17, TE p. 18

false   48. Whitman reveals the source of truth in "A Noiseless Patient Spider."
p. 17, TE p. 19

true   49. Whitman's most famous collection of poetry is called *Leaves of Grass*.
p. 18

false   50. In "The Spider and the Wasp," Petrunkevitch proves that instinct plays no part in the
p. 22   intelligent wasp's actions.

Essay

In one or more paragraphs, completely answer the question below, using examples from selections in this unit. You may use your own paper.

51. Choose one prose selection from this unit ("Dawn in the Forest," "What Stumped the Bluejays," "The Fly," or "The Spider and the Wasp") to show that prose as well as poetry can make use of imaginative comparisons. Tell what you think the author of the selection achieves by his use of these comparisons.

   Key ideas: Students' answers will vary. If they choose to discuss "The Spider and the Wasp," they

   should point out that Petrunkevitch does not use imaginative comparisons to the same degree that the

   other authors do in the unit because the purpose of his writing is to inform. He does use simile, most

   notably in his comparison of a spider's inability to change its technique of building a web with an in-

   experienced man's inability to build a bridge across a chasm. In the other three selections, the authors

   use many comparisons that the students can discuss. In many cases these comparisons help to point

   out shortcomings in human behavior. pp. 5-6, 7-10, 15, 19-23

TEST 2

Multiple Choice

Choose the best answer from the choices given.

_C_　1. Lines or parts of lines showing a similarity of sound from the vowel of the last accented
p. 27　　syllable onward are said to contain

    A. meter.
    B. alliteration.
    C. rhyme.
    D. consonance.

_A_　2. The repetition of initial consonant sounds in accented syllables is called
p. 27

    A. alliteration.
    B. consonance.
    C. meter.
    D. assonance.

_D_　3. The repetition of terminal consonant sounds in accented syllables is called
p. 27

    A. alliteration.
    B. assonance.
    C. rhyme.
    D. consonance.

_B_　4. In "All Day I Hear," the repetition of the long *o* sound is an example of
p. 28

    A. alliteration.
    B. assonance.
    C. metaphor.
    D. consonance.

_B_　5. The words *moan, alone, monotone* and *go, below, fro* in "All Day I Hear" help to create
p. 28　　a mood of

    A. pessimism.
    B. melancholy.
    C. joy.
    D. frivolity.

_B_　6. The use of words that sound like what they mean is called
p. 28

    A. alliteration.
    B. onomatopoeia.
    C. consonance.
    D. assonance.

_A_　7. In "Winter Ocean," Updike's calling the ocean a "tub / of male whales" shows the poet's
p. 29　　use of

    A. metaphor.
    B. simile.
    C. personification.
    D. alliteration.

___C___
p. 29

8. When he calls the ocean a "maker of worn wood," Updike is using

    A. assonance.
    B. consonance.
    C. alliteration.
    D. onomatopoeia.

___C___
TE p. 29

9. The speaker's tone in "Winter Ocean" is one of

    A. admiration.
    B. awe.
    C. defiance.
    D. fear.

___D___
p. 30

10. The repetition of the words "Clangity-clang" shows Colcord's use of

    A. consonance.
    B. simile.
    C. metaphor.
    D. onomatopoeia.

___B___
p. 30

11. What imaginative comparison is used in the following description of Captain Blair's ship: "The spirit of battle had gone from her, the youth, the energy, the power"?

    A. onomatopoeia
    B. personification
    C. metonymy
    D. simile

___A___
p. 30

12. The only aspect of his ship that does *not* cause Captain Blair concern is

    A. the ship's lack of proper navigational equipment.
    B. the ship's age.
    C. the ship's cargo.
    D. the ship's deteriorating condition.

___C___
p. 30

13. Captain Blair's main reason for wanting to bring the ship quickly into port is

    A. to protect his reputation as an able seaman.
    B. to keep his ship from needing extensive repairs.
    C. to get help for his ailing wife.
    D. to get the money for hauling the nitrate.

___B___
p. 31

14. The ship's crew is forced to pump constantly as a result of

    A. the waves that flood the deck during the storm.
    B. a leak the ship springs without warning.
    C. the ship's inability to make any progress.
    D. the captain's orders to get into port as quickly as possible.

___A___
p. 33

15. Which statement best describes the captain's wife's attitude toward the sea?

    A. She is not cut out for life at sea.
    B. She shares her husband's enthusiasm for life at sea.
    C. She resents her husband's love for the sea.
    D. She wants her husband to give up his seagoing life.

__C__
pp. 33-34,
TE p. 31

16. The main conflict in "The Leak" is

    A. man against nature.
    B. man against man.
    C. man against himself.
    D. man against God.

__D__
p. 40

17. Captain Blair asks God's forgiveness because he

    A. doubted that his wife would get well.
    B. made his wife undergo the hardships of life at sea.
    C. doubted that the ship would survive the storm.
    D. resented God's making them endure such hardships at sea.

__B__
p. 41

18. In Shakespeare's "Storm Fury," the storm's power is seen in all the following ways *except*

    A. the shaking of the battlements.
    B. the sinking of the ship.
    C. the ocean's figurative pelting of the clouds.
    D. the surge's figurative casting of water on the constellation.

__A__
p. 41

19. What sound repetition does Shakespeare use in the words *mountains melt* and *burning Bear?*

    A. alliteration
    B. consonance
    C. assonance
    D. rhythm

__B__
p. 41

20. In "Storm Fury" what sound repetition does the poet use in the words *ribs* and *mountains?*

    A. alliteration
    B. consonance
    C. assonance
    D. rhythm

__C__
p. 43

21. The choice to which Whitman refers in "Had I the Choice" is the choice between

    A. attempting to achieve the fame of his predecessors or remaining obscure.
    B. pleasing his readers or pleasing himself.
    C. following the pattern of his predecessors or attempting to capture the motion and mood of the sea through his verse.
    D. spending his time writing poetry or spending his time communing with the ocean.

__D__
p. 45

22. In the opening paragraph of "The Fruits of Toil," the author sets the scene by

    A. giving background information about Solomon and Priscilla.
    B. showing the unyielding nature of both the wilderness and the sea.
    C. describing the sense of hopelessness felt by the fishermen when they contemplate the future.
    D. showing the eternal tamelessness of the sea.

C
p. 45
23. In "The Fruits of Toil," Luke Dart is willing to make a compact with Solomon Stride because he

   A. owes Solomon a favor.
   B. knows that Solomon will repay the debt during the coming fishing season.
   C. trusts Solomon to repay the debt whenever he can do so.
   D. expects to profit greatly from Solomon's hard work.

C
p. 45
24. Within a few months after making the compact with Luke, Solomon does all of the following *except*

   A. get married.
   B. build his trap.
   C. repay his debt to Luke.
   D. build a cottage.

B
p. 46
25. Priscilla can best be described as a

   A. vindictive, domineering wife.
   B. loving, submissive wife.
   C. timid, unresponsive wife.
   D. patient but pessimistic wife.

A
p. 47
26. All of the following are true about Solomon Stride as he approaches middle age *except*

   A. he finally catches three quintals of fish.
   B. he still is indebted to Luke Dart.
   C. he still dreams great dreams.
   D. he and Priscilla are happy.

C
p. 48
27. As Solomon reaches old age, he becomes a "prey for the young sea" because of a deterioration in his

   A. mental ability.
   B. optimism.
   C. physical condition.
   D. strong, encouraging relationship with his wife.

Short Answer

Write the word or phrase that best answers the question.

28. What does the term *meter* mean? <u>the arrangement of accented syllables that occur at fairly equal</u>

    <u>intervals, p. 26</u>

29. What are the units of meter called? <u>poetic feet, p. 26</u>

30. What is the term for poetry that uses neither meter nor rhyme? <u>free verse, p. 27</u>

31. The words *scud-thumper* and *tub* in the first line of "Winter Ocean" make use of what poetic

    device? <u>assonance, p. 29</u>

32. What final insult does the speaker hurl at the ocean in "Winter Ocean"? <u>his taunt that the</u>

    <u>ocean is a "wind-slave," p. 29</u>

33. In what season of the year does "The Leak" take place? _winter, p. 30_

34. In "The Leak" why does the captain order his men to stop the pumps when he hears the tugboat coming? _so that the crew of the tugboat will not know the ship is leaking, p. 39_

35. For what object are the speakers in "Storm Fury" looking? _a ship, p. 41_

36. In "Storm Fury" what type of imaginative comparison is Montano using in his statement "the wind hath spoke aloud at land"? _personification, pp. 4, 41_

37. Walt Whitman was most influential in his use of what verse form? _free verse, p. 43_

38. Whom or what does the speaker address in "Had I the Choice"? _the sea, p. 43_

39. What effect does Whitman wish to create in "Had I the Choice"? _the motion and mood of the sea, p. 43_

40. In "The Fruits of Toil," why does Priscilla think Solomon can reveal the mystery of the seven thunders as he approaches death? _because she thinks that as one dies, he has visions and receives revelations, pp. 51-52_

True/False

If the statement is completely true, write *true.* **If any part of the statement is false, write** *false.*

___true___ 41. Patterned repetition of all types is more common in poetry than in prose.
p. 26

___false___ 42. The words *clasps* and *crag* illustrate both alliteration and consonance.
p. 27

___false___ 43. In "The Leak" Captain Blair refuses to pay the price the tugboat captain demands.
p. 39

___true___ 44. "Storm Fury" is a passage from Shakespeare's *Othello.*
p. 41

___false___ 45. Whitman followed closely the subject matter and form of the dominant poetic tradition.
p. 43, TE p. 43

___false___ 46. In "The Fruits of Toil," Solomon and Priscilla lose all hope after Solomon's net is destroyed.
p. 46

___false___ 47. Solomon and Priscilla consider themselves poor.
p. 48

___false___ 48. Solomon and Luke Dart both catch a glimpse of the "ship for souls" that approaches as Solomon nears death.
p. 51

___false___ 49. Solomon finally repays his debt to Luke Dart.
p. 51

___true___ 50. As he is dying, Solomon expresses gratitude for the blessings God has given him and Priscilla.
p. 52

Essay

In one or more paragraphs, completely answer the question below. You may use your own paper.

51. Identify the meter in the following lines of poetry. Also identify any repetitions of sound or syntax contained in the lines.

    A. "He clasps the crag with crooked hands."
    B. "Methinks the wind hath spoke aloud at land."
    C. "To the work! to the work! we are servants of God."
    D. "Channels only, blessed Saviour."

    Key ideas: You may wish to list for the students on the board or overhead the types of metrical feet

    and terms for feet per line listed in the TE on p. 26 rather than having them memorize these items.

    This section then tests their ability to apply the terms, not memorize them. (A) The meter is iambic

    tetrameter. The line contains alliteration (clasps, crag, crooked), assonance (clasps, crag, hands), and

    consonance (clasps, hands, land). (B) The meter is iambic pentameter. The line contains assonance

    (methinks, wind), consonance (wind, aloud), and alliteration (aloud, land). (C) The meter is anapestic

    tetrameter. The line contains the repetition of the phrase "To the work!" (D) The meter is trochaic

    tetrameter. pp. 26, 41, "To the Work," "Channels Only"

Multiple Choice

Choose the best answer from the choices given.

<u>C</u>
pp. 58-59

1. In "It Sifts from Leaden Sieves," the snow and the landscape are compared respectively to
   A. an aging woman and a cosmetician-seamstress.
   B. leaden sieves and a queen.
   C. a cosmetician-seamstress and an aging woman.
   D. a queen and leaden sieves.

<u>B</u>
pp. 58-59

2. Which statement about the arrangement in "It Sifts from Leaden Sieves" is incorrect?
   A. Each sentence begins with the same subject.
   B. The subject's actions are arranged spatially.
   C. The order of details is determined by a metaphor that extends throughout the poem.
   D. The order is controlled by the work of the cosmetician-seamstress rather than by the actual process of the snowfall.

<u>B</u>
pp. 27, 60

3. What device of sound repetition does Whittier use in the following line from "Snow-Bound": "It sank from sight before it set"?
   A. assonance
   B. alliteration
   C. rhyme
   D. onomatopoeia

<u>A</u>
TE p. 60

4. Which item does *not* apply to "Snow-Bound"?
   A. unrhymed iambic pentameter
   B. sensory images
   C. metaphoric expressions
   D. parallelism

<u>B</u>
p. 61

5. Which image does the snow-covered landscape *not* evoke in the mind of the speaker in "Snow-Bound"?
   A. an old man
   B. an aging woman
   C. a Chinese roof
   D. Pisa's leaning tower

<u>C</u>
p. 62

6. In "Snow-Bound" what makes the boys think of "Aladdin's wondrous cave"?
   A. the barn in which the animals are stranded
   B. the house in which the family is stranded
   C. the tunnel the boys create when they clear the path to the barn
   D. a story someone tells by the fireside

<u>A</u>
pp. 4, 62

7. In Whittier's statement that one of the sheep is "like Egypt's Amun roused from sleep," the poet is using
   A. a simile.
   B. metonymy.
   C. a metaphor.
   D. synecdoche.

TEST 3

__C__
pp. 4, 63

8. Whittier's labeling of the sun as a "snow-blown traveller" is an example of

    A. onomatopoeia.
    B. metonymy.
    C. personification.
    D. alliteration.

__C__
pp. 64-65

9. Which of the following biographical facts does *not* apply to Whittier?

    A. His family was known for simple Quaker values.
    B. His greatest poem, "Snow-Bound," was not written until he was almost sixty.
    C. His best works are based on memories of his life in Iowa.
    D. He wrote approximately one hundred hymn texts near the end of his life.

__C__
p. 65

10. Both "Snow-Bound" and "Winter" contain all the following contrasts *except* the contrast between

    A. indoors and outdoors.
    B. day and night.
    C. the peaceful fireside scene and the cold, blustery weather outside.
    D. cold and warmth.

__A__
pp. 66-67, 69,
TE p. 66

11. In "An Old-Fashioned Iowa Christmas," Engle's repeated use of the statement, "There are no such . . . any more" shows his use of

    A. parallelism.
    B. metonymy.
    C. synecdoche.
    D. metaphor.

__D__
pp. 66-67,
71

12. The sound Engle associates most with an Iowa Christmas is the sound of

    A. the horses stamping the soft snow.
    B. church bells.
    C. the hissing sound of the sled runners.
    D. sleigh bells.

__C__
pp. 4, 69

13. What type of imaginative comparison does Engle use in his statement that the previous summer the goose was "hissing and darting out its bill at the end of its curving neck like a feathered snake"?

    A. personification
    B. metonymy
    C. simile
    D. synecdoche

__D__
p. 69

14. The Christmas goose served all of the following purposes *except* as

    A. food.
    B. bedding.
    C. a cough remedy.
    D. clothing.

__D__
p. 70

15. According to Engle, the best "way to thank the Lord for His abundance" is to

    A. share one's abundance with others.
    B. share the holidays with family members.
    C. begin the Christmas celebration in a barn.
    D. eat the meal in the same room in which it is cooked.

_____A_____ 16. Which statement about the organization of "Snow in the Suburbs" is *not* correct?
  p. 72

    A. The movement is from animate to inanimate.
    B. The movement is from impersonal to personal.
    C. The movement is from humorous to serious.
    D. The movement is from general to specific.

_____C_____ 17. Which item best states the theme of "Snow in the Suburbs"?
  p. 72

    A. Inclement weather has an adverse effect on animals.
    B. Both animate and inanimate objects feel the effects of a snowstorm.
    C. Man has a duty to the helpless.
    D. God has created animals to withstand the adverse effects of nature.

_____D_____ 18. In the line "A black cat comes, wide-eyed and thin," Hardy uses both
  pp. 27, 72

    A. alliteration and consonance.
    B. assonance and onomatopoeia.
    C. consonance and onomatopoeia.
    D. assonance and alliteration.

_____D_____ 19. "The Return of the Rangers" includes the statement "The red squirrel chirred." The
  pp. 4, 76   word *chirred* is an example of

    A. personification.
    B. metonymy.
    C. synecdoche.
    D. onomatopoeia.

_____A_____ 20. The woodcutters who help the men get to shore at Number Four stare at them because
  p. 82   of the group's

    A. shocking physical appearance.
    B. refusal to identify themselves.
    C. belligerent behavior.
    D. strange manner of dress.

_____A_____ 21. The *best* statement of a theme concerning leadership in "The Return of the Rangers"
  p. 84   is that a good leader will

    A. sacrifice his needs for those of his subordinates.
    B. lead his followers out of a situation if danger is approaching.
    C. act without taking advice from his subordinates.
    D. realize his own limitations and delegate responsibilities to others.

Short Answer

Write the word or phrase that best answers the question.

22. What are the "It" and the "Sieves" in "It Sifts from Leaden Sieves"? ___*the snow and the clouds,*___
                   p. 58

23. What period of time is covered in the excerpt from "Snow-Bound"? ___*two days, pp. 60-61, 63, TE*___
                   p. 60

24. Americans found "Snow-Bound" comforting as they recovered from what war? *the Civil War, p. 64*

25. The song "Winter" is from what Shakespearean play? *Love's Labour's Lost, p. 65*

26. What theme or themes do Whittier's "Snow-Bound" and Shakespeare's "Winter" both express? *Work and duty precede rest and leisure; quality of life is more dependent on inward character than on outward circumstances (either answer). TE p. 65*

27. In the line "Every fork like a white web-foot," what type of imaginative comparison does Hardy use? *simile, pp. 4, 72*

28. Briefly describe the organization of the stanzas of "I Will Praise the Lord at All Times." *winter to autumn and then morning to night, p. 86*

29. In "The Return of the Rangers," why does Stephens leave with the food before Rogers and his men arrive? *He thinks the shots fired by Rogers and his men are shots fired by the French and Indians. p. 84*

30. In "The Return of the Rangers," what does Rogers plan to do before confronting Stephens about fleeing with the food? *personally help deliver food to his starving troops up the river, p. 84*

31. The climax of Cowper's light imagery in "I Will Praise the Lord at All Times" occurs in the stanza referring to what season? *summer, p. 86*

True/False

If the statement is completely true, write *true*. If any part of the statement is false, write *false*.

true   32. Thomas Hardy's outlook in his writings was typically one of gloom.
p. 73

true   33. The power and simplicity of Cowper's best poetry reflect the Bible's influence on him.
p. 87

TEST 3

Matching I

Match each quotation with the work from which it is taken. Each answer will be used more than once.

      A. It Sifts from Leaden Sieves
      B. Snow-Bound
      C. Winter
      D. An Old-Fashioned Iowa Christmas
      E. Snow in the Suburbs

B *p. 60*   34. The sun that brief December day / Rose cheerless over hills of gray

C *p. 65*   35. Then nightly sings the staring owl, / "Tu-whit, tu-who!"

B *p. 64*   36. The great throat of the chimney laughed

E *p. 72*   37. Some flakes have lost their way, and grope back upward

D *p. 67*   38. A barn with the cattle and horses is the place to begin Christmas.

B *p. 64*   39. Blow high, blow low, not all its snow / Could quench our hearth fire's ruddy glow.

C *p. 65*   40. And Marian's nose looks red and raw

A *p. 58*   41. It fills with alabaster wool / The wrinkles of the road.

A *p. 58*   42. Unbroken forehead from the east / Unto the east again.

D *p. 71*   43. But the one great star in the East never wavered.

E *p. 72*   44. A snow-lump thrice his own slight size / Descends on him and showers his head and eyes

Matching II

Match each author with his or her description. Answers will be used once or not at all.

      A. William Cowper
      B. Emily Dickinson
      C. Paul Engle
      D. Thomas Hardy
      E. Kenneth Roberts
      F. William Shakespeare
      G. John Greenleaf Whittier

G *pp. 64-65*   45. New Englander who wrote nearly 100 hymn texts

C *p. 71*   46. successor to Walt Whitman's optimistic style; believed in the values of the "American Dream"

D *p. 73*   47. writer of great technical skill and emotional power whose works are marked by an appreciation of nature and a tone of despair

E *p. 85*   48. journalist from Maine who became one of America's most talented historical novelists

_____A_____ 49. evangelical English poet who said, "God made the country, and man made the town"
p. 87

_____F_____ 50. wrote *Love's Labour's Lost* and *Othello*
pp. 41, 65

Essay

In one or more paragraphs, completely answer the question below, using examples from selections in this unit. You may use your own paper.

51. Discuss at least one pleasant aspect of nature the authors present in "It Sifts from Leaden Sieves," "Snow-Bound," and "An Old-Fashioned Iowa Christmas." Discuss at least one unpleasant aspect of nature the authors present in "Winter," "Snow in the Suburbs," and "The Return of the Rangers." What application regarding both aspects of nature can you make based on the theme of "I Will Praise the Lord at All Times"?

Key ideas: In "It Sifts from Leaden Sieves" and "Snow-Bound," the snow covers the landscape and in doing so appeals to the imagination. In "Snow-Bound" the snowfall provides the opportunity for the family to experience being together and also to participate in hard but satisfying work. In "An Old-Fashioned Iowa Christmas," riding through the snow and playing in the snow after the dinner provide the author with comforting memories for a lifetime. In "Winter," the poet shows such adverse effects as the shepherd's cold hands, the frozen milk, the coughing that drowns out the preacher's message, and the girl's red, raw nose. In "Snow in the Suburbs," nature presents hardship to both the sparrow and the cat, and in "The Return of the Rangers," the waterfall and the icy water make life miserable for the rangers. The title "I Will Praise the Lord at All Times" expresses the poem's theme that all aspects of nature should cause one to praise the Creator. pp. 58-59, 60-64, 65, 66-67, 70-71, 72, 80, 86

TEST 4

Multiple Choice

Choose the best answer from the choices given.

_D_
pp. 27, 94

1. In "The Donkey" Chesterton's use of the words *fishes* and *figs* shows

    A. assonance, consonance, and onomatopoeia.
    B. consonance, onomatopoeia, and alliteration.
    C. assonance, alliteration, and onomatopoeia.
    D. assonance, alliteration, and consonance.

_B_
pp. 95-98

2. In "Cupid's Arrows" Kitty Beighton can be described by all of the following adjectives *except*

    A. pretty.
    B. submissive.
    C. poor.
    D. skillful.

_A_
pp. 95-98,
TE p. 97

3. The character in "Cupid's Arrows" who best illustrates the precedence of false values is

    A. Mrs. Beighton.
    B. Mr. Beighton.
    C. Kitty Beighton.
    D. Anthony Barr-Saggott.

_A_
p. 96

4. Which statement does *not* describe Kitty Beighton's feelings toward Barr-Saggott?

    A. She was able to overlook his ugliness.
    B. She was flattered that the other girls had bad feelings toward her.
    C. She was impressed that he was a Commissioner with letters after his name.
    D. She was flattered that he was always at her feet.

_B_
p. 98,
TE p. 96

5. Which statement best expresses the theme of "Cupid's Arrows"?

    A. Outward appearance is not as important as inward beauty.
    B. Love is more important than position and material possessions in the choice of a mate.
    C. Parents should do what is best for their children.
    D. There are times when a person should not try to do his or her best.

_D_
p. 99

6. As he grows older, the knight in "Eldorado" becomes

    A. disoriented.
    B. bitter.
    C. apathetic.
    D. weary.

_B_
pp. 100-1

7. In "The Progress of Poesy," Arnold's attitude toward aging is one of

    A. acceptance.
    B. despair.
    C. nonchalance.
    D. arrogance.

__B__
pp. 102-3

8. Which sentence is the topic sentence of Chesterton's essay?

   A. "Even as we are dying, the whole world is coming to life."
   B. "There are advantages in the advance through middle age into later life which are very seldom stated in a sensible way."
   C. "It is a true proverb, no doubt, which says 'There is no fool like an old fool.' "
   D. "I have lived to see the dead proverbs come alive."

__C__
p. 103

9. In Chesterton's statement that the young feel that they are being "stuffed with stale things," the "stale things" to which he refers are

   A. antiquated theories.
   B. historical facts.
   C. traditions and proverbs.
   D. prejudices.

__B__
p. 103

10. In his essay on aging, Chesterton alludes to the decline of the Roman and Spanish empires to show that

   A. what one learns in childhood remains with him.
   B. present and future societies should learn from past ones.
   C. one can escape from the present by reliving the past.
   D. past civilizations were superior to present ones.

__A__
pp. 102-4

11. Which conclusion do the authors of "On the Pleasures of No Longer Being Very Young" and "The Soul's Dark Cottage" both share?

   A. Old age brings greater insight.
   B. Old age brings bitterness.
   C. Old age brings with it a loss of creativity.
   D. Old age enables one to view eternity better.

__B__
p. 4,
TE pp. 103-4

12. In "The Soul's Dark Cottage," Waller's comparison of the body to a dilapidated cottage and of death to the crossing of a river are examples of

   A. personification.
   B. metaphor.
   C. synecdoche.
   D. metonymy.

__B__
p. 109

13. In "Pigeon Feathers," David's mother's attitude toward Granmom is one of

   A. pity.
   B. irritation.
   C. understanding.
   D. patience.

__C__
p. 110

14. David's experience at the outhouse is especially frightening because he

   A. is reminded of the science fiction books he has read.
   B. is deathly afraid of spiders.
   C. is afraid his beliefs have been based on error and that death is annihilation.
   D. knows that no one understands what he is experiencing.

TEST 4

_C_ 15. Which aspect of the definition of the word *soul* interests David most?
p. 111

    A. the Greek and Egyptian conceptions
    B. the idea that the soul is the "animating principle" of life
    C. the idea that the soul is "separate in nature from the body and usually held to be separable in existence"
    D. the idea that the soul is "manifested in psychical activities"

_B_ 16. David's mother's prejudice against working on Sunday consoles him because he is
p. 113

    A. not in the mood to do manual labor.
    B. searching for any confirmation of the validity of his faith.
    C. unsure of his mother's religious beliefs.
    D. looking for an opportunity to talk to her.

_B_ 17. David is excited about attending the catechism class in Firetown because he
p. 113

    A. wants to meet other young people.
    B. is looking for the "nod" or "gesture" that he needs.
    C. wants to get away from his parents' constant bickering.
    D. thinks it will be superior to the one in Olinger.

Short Answer

Write the word or phrase that best answers the question or defines the term.

18. What is an allusion? *a reference within a written work to something outside it, p. 92*

19. Name two of the unusual circumstances that supposedly existed at the time of the birth of the donkey's species. *"fishes flew," "forests walked," "figs grew upon thorns," or "the moon was blood" (any two), p. 94*

20. In "The Donkey," who is pictured as the mocker of what God has created? *the Devil, p. 94*

21. In what country does "Cupid's Arrows" take place? *India, p. 95*

22. In "Cupid's Arrows" to what mythological goddess of the forest is Kitty compared and why is this comparison an appropriate one? *Diana; both are skilled in archery. p. 96*

23. At the tournament in "Cupid's Arrows," what does Kitty do that surprises everyone? *misses most of her shots on purpose, p. 98*

24. In "Eldorado" to what is the "pilgrim shadow" alluding in his reference to the "valley of the shadow"? *the "valley of the shadow of death" in the Twenty-third Psalm, p. 99, TE p. 100*

25. What is the meaning of the word *poesy* in Arnold's "The Progress of Poesy"? *the creative imagination in general and poetry in particular, TE p. 99*

26. In "The Progress of Poesy," the reference to smiting the rock to bring forth water is an allusion to what Biblical character? <u>Moses, TE p. 100</u>

27. What three stages of the poet's life does Arnold describe in "The Progress of Poesy"? <u>youth, middle age, and old age, p. 100</u>

28. According to Chesterton in "On the Pleasures of No Longer Being Very Young," why has the world repeated proverbs? <u>because they are practical, p. 103</u>

29. From "Pigeon Feathers" name at least three things David finds offensive in H. G. Wells's account of Jesus. <u>the characterization of Jesus as a hobo, the use of the small h in the pronouns referring to Him, the claim that Jesus accidentally survived His crucifixion, the springing up of a new religion as a result of this "accident," the accounts of the miracles' being results of "the credulous imagination of the times," and the contradiction between the historical Jesus and the theology that was formulated about Him (any three), p. 108</u>

30. Reverend Dobson tells David that he should think of heaven in what way? <u>"as the way the goodness Abraham Lincoln did lives after him," p. 114</u>

31. According to David's mother, who made God? <u>man, p. 116</u>

32. What does David observe that finally gives him the certainty for which he has been searching? <u>the patterns of the pigeons' feathers, pp. 122-23</u>

True/False

If the statement is completely true, write *true*. If any part of the statement is false, write *false*.

<u>false</u> 33. Chesterton shows his contempt for the donkey in his poem.
p. 94

<u>true</u> 34. G. K. Chesterton valued the family unit and was optimistic in his writings.
pp. 94-95

<u>true</u> 35. The word *shadow* appears with a slightly different meaning in each stanza of
p. 99   "Eldorado."

<u>false</u> 36. G. K. Chesterton agrees with Matthew Arnold's view of the advantages of youth over age.
p. 102

<u>true</u> 37. "The Soul's Dark Cottage" answers the objection that creative powers fail when one
p. 104   reaches old age.

<u>false</u> 38. David's final assurance that he will live forever is based on his personal faith in Christ.
p. 123,
TE p. 123

TEST 4

Matching I

Match each character from "Pigeon Feathers" below with his or her description.

A. Mother
B. Father
C. Granmom
D. Dobson
E. David

___C___ 39. manages wonderfully, in spite of his or her "waggler"
pp. 109, 112

___B___ 40. represents the modernistic view of science as god
p. 105

___A___ 41. represents the Romantic view of life
p. 105

___D___ 42. believes that after death "our souls are asleep"
p. 114

___E___ 43. searches for truth
p. 105

Matching II

Match each selection below with the allusion that appears in the selection.

A. Cupid's Arrows
B. The Donkey
C. Eldorado
D. On the Pleasures of No Longer Being Very Young
E. Pigeon Feathers
F. The Progress of Poesy
G. The Soul's Dark Cottage

___B___ 44. Palm Sunday
p. 94

___A___ 45. the Judgment of Paris
p. 97

___C___ 46. Psalm 23
p. 99

___F___ 47. Moses' smiting the rock to bring forth water
p. 100

___D___ 48. Napoleon
p. 103

___G___ 49. Moses' viewing the Promised Land from Mount Pisgah
TE p. 103

___E___ 50. *The Time Machine*
p. 106

Essay

In one or more paragraphs, completely answer the question below. You may use your own paper.

51. Give one example each of a literary, a historical, and a Biblical allusion from the selections in the unit. Discuss the significance of each allusion to the story or poem.

Key ideas: Examples of allusions will vary. One example of a literary allusion is the allusion to H. G. Wells in "Pigeon Feathers." H. G. Wells's comments on Jesus provide the conflict that David must solve, and the reference to his Time Machine relates to the growing fear that David experiences as his doubts increase. An example of a historical allusion is the allusion to Napoleon or King Charles in "On the Importance of No Longer Being Very Young." These allusions point out the deadness Chesterton says that the young associate with maxims and proverbs of the past. An example of a Biblical allusion is the allusion to the triumphal entry in "The Donkey." This allusion relates to the theme of God's using unlikely vessels to convey His truth. (Note that students may use examples of allusions referred to on this test; however, the essay will test their ability to discuss the significance of the allusions. Make sure each allusion truly fits its category—literary, historical, or Biblical.) pp. 94, 103, 108, 110

TEST 5

Name_____

Multiple Choice

Choose the best answer from the choices given.

__B__
p. 127

1. An extended metaphor in which the characters, incidents, and situations have a meaning beyond the literal level of the narrative is called a/an

   A. symbol.
   B. allegory.
   C. analogy.
   D. fable.

__C__
p. 128

2. An allegorical story with two or more strictly correlated levels of meaning is called a/an

   A. fable.
   B. analogy.
   C. parable.
   D. symbol.

__D__
p. 131

3. The adjective that best describes the ant in "The Ant and the Grasshopper" is

   A. slothful.
   B. selfless.
   C. compassionate.
   D. industrious.

__A__
p. 131

4. The ant chides the grasshopper primarily for his lack of

   A. foresight.
   B. intelligence.
   C. courage.
   D. compassion.

__D__
TE p. 131

5. The seasonal metaphor in "The Ant and the Grasshopper" corresponds to

   A. times of good weather and adverse weather.
   B. the changes that occur as a person ages.
   C. the ant's biological life cycle.
   D. times of prosperity and adversity.

__C__
p. 137

6. The title "maggie and milly and molly and may" illustrates the poetic device called

   A. personification.
   B. assonance.
   C. alliteration.
   D. onomatopoeia.

__A__
p. 137,
TE p. 137

7. Cummings's poetry is unconventional in its lack of all the following *except*

   A. alliteration.
   B. capitalization.
   C. punctuation.
   D. spacing around internal punctuation.

B
p. 139

8. The attitude of Prince Prospero and his revelers toward those outside the abbey was

    A. sympathetic.
    B. indifferent.
    C. hostile.
    D. benevolent.

B
pp. 4, 92, 144

9. Choose the literary device that does *not* appear in the following sentence referring to the Red Death: "He [the Red Death] had come like a thief in the night."

    A. simile
    B. synecdoche
    C. allusion
    D. personification

B
p. 145

10. Browning makes all the following assertions about his special star *except* that

    A. it throws red and blue darts.
    B. his friends enjoy watching it with him.
    C. he loves it.
    D. it has opened its soul to him.

C
p. 145

11. Which statement about the symbolism of Browning's special star is correct?

    A. He identifies the star as Elizabeth Barrett Browning.
    B. He identifies the star as his religious faith.
    C. He does not identify the symbolism of his star.
    D. He identifies the symbolism of his star to his friends only.

Short Answer

Write the word or phrase that best answers the question or defines the term.

12. To what three things does Browning compare his star? *a spar (mineral), a bird, and a flower, p. 145*

13. Define the word *epigram*. *a short, highly compressed poem making a wise or humorous observation and ending with a witty twist, TE p. 130*

14. Define the term *fable*. *a story in which the details support the meaning collectively; may include a stated moral, pp. 128, 139*

15. According to its literary definition, what does a symbol represent? *something in addition to itself, p. 126*

16. To what is the poet alluding in "Epigram" by his Biblical references to dust and to rainbows? *God's creation of man from dust and His covenant that man would never again be destroyed by a flood, p. 130*

17. In Keats's poem the insects' songs are symbolic of what? *man's poetry, p. 132*

TEST 5

18. What function of poetry does each animal represent in "The Nightingale and the Glowworm"?
    the aesthetic or for the purpose of beauty (nightingale), the didactic function or teaching (glowworm),
    pp. 133-35, TE pp. 132-33

19. What does the squirrel say he can do that the mountain cannot do, and what is that action's symbolic meaning? *crack a nut; solve difficult philosophical problems, p. 136, TE p. 137*

20. What does the squirrel say that the mountain can do that he cannot do, and what is the symbolic meaning of that ability? *carry forests on his back; conventional public opinion, pp. 136-37, TE p. 137*

21. What character trait does Milly's befriending of the "stranded star" illustrate? *concern and compassion for living things, p. 137*

22. What does Molly's discovery of a "horrible thing" at the beach show about her personality?
    that she is fearful and excitable, p. 137, TE p. 138

23. What colors were the first and last rooms of Prince Prospero's abbey, and what do the colors symbolize? *blue, which symbolizes birth, and black, which represents death, p. 140, TE p. 140*

24. What reaction did the revelers have to the chiming of the ebony clock each hour? *nervousness and meditation on mortality, p. 141*

25. What specifically does the corpselike masquerader at the ball symbolize? *the Red Death, p. 142*

True/False

If the statement is completely true, write *true*. If any part of the statement is false, write *false*.

true
p. 129
26. Most good imaginative literature is to some degree symbolic.

false
pp. 131-32
27. Aesop in his fable and Keats in his poem share the same view of the grasshopper.

true
p. 132
28. "The Grasshopper and the Cricket" is arranged structurally according to seasons of the year.

false
p. 137
29. Emerson believed that universal truth could be discovered only through Scripture.

true
pp. 136-37,
TE pp. 137-38
30. Both Emerson's "Fable" and Cummings's "maggie and milly and molly and may" have stated morals.

false
p. 139
31. Prince Prospero was fearful and unhappy when he entered the abbey with his friends.

true
p. 145,
TE p. 145
32. In "My Star" Browning's allusion to Saturn can be interpreted more than one way.

Matching I

Match the following selections with the correct themes or morals.

A. The Ant and the Grasshopper
B. Epigram
C. Fable
D. The Grasshopper and the Cricket
E. maggie and milly and molly and may
F. The Masque of the Red Death
G. My Star
H. The Nightingale and the Glowworm

___C___ 33. "Talents differ."
p. 136

___F___ 34. Death is inescapable.
p. 144

___B___ 35. Without the presence of trials in life, one would not appreciate its joyful aspects.
p. 130

___G___ 36. Nearly everyone has some object or idea that fascinates him.
p. 145

___A___ 37. "It is thrifty to prepare today for the wants of tomorrow."
p. 131

___H___ 38. Both the aesthetic and didactic functions of poetry contribute to poetry's ability to make
p. 135, life more tolerable.
TE pp. 132-33

___E___ 39. "For whatever we lose(like a you or a me) / it's always ourselves we find in the sea."
p. 137

___D___ 40. Poetry is possible even in the winter, or the unpleasant circumstances, of life.
TE p. 132

Matching II

Match the following symbols with the objects or ideas the symbols represent.

A. ant
B. black room with red panes
C. blue room
D. cricket
E. dust
F. glowworm
G. grasshopper
H. nightingale
 I. rainbow
J. squirrel

___H___ 41. the aesthetic function of poetry
TE p. 133

___I___ 42. the hopeful, joyous part of life
TE p. 131

___B___ 43. the Red Death
TE p. 140

___J___ 44. a moral philosopher
TE p. 137

___C___ 45. birth
TE p. 140

TEST 5

<u>A</u> 46. a thrifty, industrious person
TE p. 131

<u>F</u> 47. the didactic function of poetry
TE p. 132

<u>D</u> 48. winter's poet
TE p. 132

<u>E</u> 49. the trials of life
TE p. 131

<u>G</u> 50. an unthrifty, slothful person
TE p. 131

Essay

In one or more paragraphs, completely answer *one* of the questions below, using examples from selections in this unit. You may use your own paper.

51a. Give two examples of insects or animals used as symbols in this unit's selections. Also, identify the selections in which the symbols appear and tell what the symbols represent.

Key ideas: Examples from Aesop's "The Ant and the Grasshopper" are the ant, representing an industrious person, and the grasshopper, representing a slothful person. In Keats's "The Grasshopper and the Cricket," the grasshopper represents the youthful or "summer" poet, and the cricket represents the aging or "winter" poet. In Cowper's "The Nightingale and the Glowworm," the nightingale represents poetry's aesthetic function, and the glowworm represents its didactic function. In Emerson's "Fable" the squirrel represents a moral philosopher. TE pp. 131-33, 137

51b. What universal theme does "The Masque of the Red Death" support? Name at least five details relating to plot, setting, or characterization that contribute to the theme.

Key ideas: The universal theme is that man cannot escape death. Many details contribute to this theme, so students' answers will vary. Some plot details are the securing of the iron gates, the merrymaking of the revelers to shut out the events, and the final confrontation of the Red Death by Prince Prospero and his followers. Some details related to setting are the walls and iron gates of the abbey; the rooms' colors, which progress from blue to black; and the rooms' design, which prevents seeing from room to room. Details related to characterization include the references to Prince Prospero's madness and eccentricities and the irony of his name. pp. 139-44; TE pp. 139-40

Multiple Choice

Choose the best answer from the choices given.

___B___
pp. 150-51

1. The terms *pun, foreshadowing,* and *understatement* all refer to types of

   A. dramatic irony.
   B. verbal irony.
   C. paradox.
   D. irony of situation.

___C___
pp. 156-57

2. The nurse first accuses Tom of being naughty because he

   A. kicks Jenny and pulls her hair.
   B. refuses to answer her questions.
   C. allows Jenny to sit by herself under the table.
   D. refuses to let Jenny play with the train.

___A___
p. 159,
TE p. 159

3. The underlying tone in "Letter from a West Texas Constituent" is one of

   A. anger.
   B. apathy.
   C. humor.
   D. despair.

___C___
pp. 160-61,
TE p. 160

4. The main target of irony in "A Considerable Speck (Microscopic)" is

   A. liberal sentimentality.
   B. man's lack of intelligence.
   C. mindless writing.
   D. man's lack of respect for living creatures.

___B___
pp. 154,
160-61

5. In both Wheelock's "Earth" and Frost's "A Considerable Speck (Microscopic),"

   A. the observers are human beings.
   B. the irony relates to human intelligence.
   C. those being observed are human beings.
   D. human intelligence is used wisely.

___B___
p. 161

6. Which statement does *not* characterize Robert Frost's poetry?

   A. He believed that poetry "ends in a clarification of life."
   B. His poetry systematically sets forth his beliefs.
   C. He frequently used human instinct as a moral guide.
   D. He believed that poetry provides a "momentary stay against confusion."

___D___
p. 162,
TE p. 162

7. The hyperbole in "Scylla Toothless" is that

   A. Scylla has lost all her teeth.
   B. Scylla is extremely ugly.
   C. Scylla has grown old.
   D. Scylla's tongue has worn her teeth away.

___D___
TE p. 163

8. The name *Scylla* is an allusion to

   A. the Bible.
   B. American folklore.
   C. an old British legend.
   D. classical mythology.

TEST 6

B
p. 162,
TE p. 163

9. The poet creates irony in "At the Aquarium" through his use of

    A. hyperbole.
    B. a reversal in perspective.
    C. a surprise ending.
    D. viewing a situation from a single viewpoint.

D
pp. 162-63,
TE p. 164

10. "At the Aquarium" illustrates Max Eastman's concept of

    A. man's ability to reach ultimate perfection through reason.
    B. "the right of the individual to make his own choices."
    C. poetry's power to provide "a momentary stay against confusion."
    D. "the lostness of modern man."

C
pp. 165-67

11. The real reason Wonder decides to leave the country is that the Viceroy

    A. fires him.
    B. assigns him to a new post.
    C. jokes about the mistake made in the Mellish-Mellishe incident.
    D. takes away his authority.

B
p. 168

12. Which of the following actions from the opening paragraphs of "The Grave Grass Quivers" does *not* foreshadow the events to follow?

    A. The narrator's shovel strikes something.
    B. Doc Martindale says his father and brother were killed in 1861.
    C. Doc Martindale says, "Murdered."
    D. "We began to uncover things."

A
pp. 171-72,
177

13. Doc Martindale is surprised by Eli Goble's gift of the park because

    A. giving gifts is inconsistent with Goble's character.
    B. Goble especially prizes the land he is giving away.
    C. Goble has promised the land to his son.
    D. the land is not suitable for a park.

C
p. 180

14. In "Yet If His Majesty, Our Sovereign Lord," the poet uses irony to compare

    A. James I to Charles I.
    B. a visit by a nobleman to a visit by a king.
    C. one's preparation for a king's visit to his preparation for Christ's visit.
    D. a king's attributes to Christ's attributes.

Short Answer

Write the word or phrase that best answers the question.

15. What two activities take place in "The Golf Links Lie So Near the Mill"? *men playing golf and children working, p. 153*

16. What characteristic does the speaker in "Earth" say Earth's inhabitants must have possessed? *high intelligence, p. 154*

17. What makes the occasion special for Tom in "A Special Occasion"? *Jenny's visit, pp. 156-57*

TEST 6

18. Discuss the specific situational irony in "A Special Occasion." *Situational irony occurs when the nurse judges the children's behavior based on her own adult perspective. pp. 156-58*

19. What does "Letter from a West Texas Constituent" satirize? *the federal government's farm subsidy program, p. 159*

20. What is the "considerable speck"? *a mite (or very small insect), p. 160*

21. What coincidence causes the ironic reversal of expectations in "A Germ Destroyer"? *Both E. Mellish and E. Mellishe are in Simla at the same time staying at the same hotel. pp. 164-67*

22. According to Doc Martindale ("The Grave Grass Quivers"), how did he know exactly where to dig? *because there were no wind-flowers on that spot, indicating that the sod had been turned, p. 179*

True/False

If the statement is completely true, write *true*. If any part of the statement is false, write *false*.

false 23. The irony in "The Golf Links Lie So Near the Mill" is directed toward the golfers.
TE p. 153

false 24. The speaker in "Earth" believes that the earth may have exploded spontaneously.
p. 154

false 25. The speaker in "Earth" is highly emotional as he makes his observations about the exploding planet.
p. 154

false 26. In "Earth" Wheelock pays a compliment to human intelligence.
p. 154, TE p. 154

true 27. The fictional speaker in "Earth" helps to give the reader a distanced perspective on himself.
p. 154,
TE pp. 154-55

true 28. Irony is an effective means of persuasion because one has trouble replying to it.
TE p. 159

true 29. In "Yet If His Majesty, Our Sovereign Lord," the poet says that one has a duty to show honor to a king.
p. 180

false 30. The poet says that we are preparing for Christ's visit in the same way that we prepare for an earthly king's visit.
p. 180

Matching I

Match the following terms with the correct definitions.

A. dramatic irony
B. foreshadowing
C. hyperbole
D. paradox
E. pun
F. sarcasm
G. satire
H. situational irony
I. structural irony
J. verbal irony

_D_ 31. a seeming contradiction
p. 148

_H_ 32. the contrast between what is reasonable to expect and what actually happens
p. 149

_A_ 33. the contrast between a reader's knowledge and a character's ignorance
p. 149

_J_ 34. language that means something other than what it actually states
p. 150

_F_ 35. verbal irony that takes the form of mock praise
p. 150

_B_ 36. prophetic irony
p. 151

_E_ 37. the use of words identical in sound but different in meaning to create a double meaning
p. 151

_G_ 38. corrective ridicule in literature
p. 151

_I_ 39. verbal irony that extends throughout an entire work
TE p. 153

_C_ 40. ironic overstatement
TE pp. 150, 162

Matching II

Match the following works with their themes.

A. At the Aquarium
B. A Considerable Speck (Microscopic)
C. Earth
D. A Germ Destroyer
E. The Golf Links Lie So Near the Mill
F. The Grave Grass Quivers
G. Letter from a West Texas Constituent
H. Scylla Toothless
I. A Special Occasion
J. Yet If His Majesty, Our Sovereign Lord

_C_ 41. Man's intelligence leads to his destruction.
p. 154

_I_ 42. Adults often misjudge childhood behavior because of an improper perspective.
p. 156

TEST 6

_G_   43. A farmer shows the absurdity of government policy.
p. 159

_B_   44. An insect shows more intelligence than some writers.
p. 160

_H_   45. Gossip is detrimental to the one who gossips.
p. 162

_A_   46. Man shares a sense of aimlessness with nonhuman creatures.
p. 162

_D_   47. A person's reputation is ruined by an embarrassing mistake.
pp. 164-67

_F_   48. A man's skill acquired from Indians reveals his guilt.
pp. 168-79

_J_   49. Man still makes no preparation for Christ's return.
p. 180

_E_   50. There is something wrong with a society that forces children to work while men play.
p. 153,
TE p. 153

Essay

In one or more paragraphs, completely answer *one* of the questions below, using examples from selections in this unit. You may use your own paper.

51a. Define the term *situational irony* and choose one story or poem from the unit that contains this type of irony. Tell specifically how the author uses this irony to achieve his desired effect.

Key ideas: Situational irony is the contrast between what is reasonably expected to happen and what

actually happens. Students' choices of selections will vary. One example is the irony of the men play-

ing while the children are working in "The Golf Links Lie So Near the Mill." The poet achieves his

purpose of condemning a society that would allow such a situation to exist. Another example is the

nurse's misjudging of the children's behavior in "A Special Occasion" because she views them from

her adult perspective. The author shows the importance of not relying on a single viewpoint. Accept

other examples that show that the students understand situational irony. pp. 149, 153, 156-58

51b. Define the term *dramatic irony*. Show how the authors of "A Special Occasion" and "A Germ Destroyer" use this type of irony.

Key ideas: Dramatic irony is the contrast between a reader's knowledge and a character's lack of

knowledge of a situation. In "A Special Occasion," the reader knows that the children are enjoying their

visit, but the nurse is not aware of this. In "A Germ Destroyer," the reader knows that Mellish has been

mistaken for Mellishe, but the characters do not realize the mistake until it is too late. pp. 149, 156-58,

164-67

51c. What is verbal irony? In which selection does the author use this irony in a mock-serious tone to persuade? Why is this technique effective?

Key ideas: Verbal irony is language that means something other than what it actually states. In "Letter from a West Texas Constituent," the author uses verbal irony throughout his letter to persuade the reader that the governmental policy of subsidizing farmers is wasteful. This technique is effective because an argument presented in this way is hard to refute. pp. 150, 159

Multiple Choice

Choose the best answer from the choices given.

___B___
p. 5
1. Identify the imaginative comparison Twain uses in the following sentence from "Dawn in the Forest": "The marvel of Nature shaking off sleep and going to work unfolded itself to the musing boy."

   A. simile
   B. personification
   C. metonymy
   D. synecdoche

___B___
p. 12
2. In "A Bird Came Down the Walk," what imaginative comparison is Dickinson using in her statement that the bird's eyes "looked like frightened Beads"?

   A. metonymy
   B. simile
   C. metaphor
   D. personification

___C___
p. 17
3. In the second stanza of "A Noiseless Patient Spider," Whitman compares the first stanza's vehicle of comparison (the spider beginning to spin its web) to

   A. the formation of a bridge.
   B. gossamer threads.
   C. the soul's search for connection and foundation.
   D. a ductile anchor.

___A___
p. 19,
TE p. 23
4. Which sentence is the thesis sentence of "The Spider and the Wasp"?

   A. "In the feeding and safeguarding of their progeny the insects and spiders exhibit some interesting analogies to reasoning and some crass examples of blind instinct."
   B. "In a Paris museum is a tropical specimen which is said to have been in captivity for 25 years."
   C. "But all spiders, and especially hairy ones, have an extremely delicate sense of touch."
   D. "In a way the instinctive urge to escape is not only easier but more efficient than reasoning."

___C___
p. 27
5. Lines or parts of lines showing a similarity of sound from the vowel of the last accented syllable onward are said to contain

   A. meter.
   B. alliteration.
   C. rhyme.
   D. consonance.

___A___
p. 27
6. The repetition of initial consonant sounds in accented syllables is called

   A. alliteration.
   B. consonance.
   C. meter.
   D. assonance.

<u>**D**</u>
p. 27

7. The repetition of terminal consonant sounds in accented syllables is called

    A. alliteration.
    B. assonance.
    C. rhyme.
    D. consonance.

<u>**B**</u>
p. 28

8. The use of words that sound like what they mean is called

    A. alliteration.
    B. onomatopoeia.
    C. consonance.
    D. assonance.

<u>**A**</u>
p. 29

9. In "Winter Ocean" Updike's calling the ocean a "tub / of male whales" shows the poet's use of

    A. metaphor.
    B. simile.
    C. personification.
    D. alliteration.

<u>**C**</u>
p. 43

10. The choice to which Whitman refers in "Had I the Choice" is the choice between

    A. attempting to achieve the fame of his predecessors or remaining obscure.
    B. pleasing his readers or pleasing himself.
    C. following the pattern of his predecessors or attempting to capture the motion and mood of the sea through his verse.
    D. spending his time writing poetry or spending his time communing with the ocean.

<u>**C**</u>
pp. 58-59

11. In "It Sifts from Leaden Sieves," the snow and landscape are compared respectively to

    A. an aging woman and a cosmetician-seamstress.
    B. leaden sieves and a queen.
    C. a cosmetician-seamstress and an aging woman.
    D. a queen and leaden sieves.

<u>**B**</u>
pp. 27, 60

12. What device of sound repetition does Whittier use in the following line from "Snow-Bound": "It sank from sight before it set"?

    A. assonance
    B. alliteration
    C. rhyme
    D. onomatopoeia

<u>**A**</u>
pp. 66-67, 69,
TE pp. 66-67

13. In "An Old-Fashioned Iowa Christmas," Engle's repeated use of the statement, "There are no such . . . any more" shows his use of

    A. parallelism.
    B. metonymy.
    C. synecdoche.
    D. metaphor.

__C__ 14. Which item best states the theme of "Snow in the Suburbs"?
p. 72

    A. Inclement weather has an adverse effect on animals.
    B. Both animate and inanimate objects feel the effects of a snowstorm.
    C. Man has a duty to the helpless.
    D. God has created animals to withstand the adverse effects of nature.

__A__ 15. The *best* statement of a theme concerning leadership in "The Return of the Rangers" is
p. 84   that a good leader will

    A. sacrifice his needs for those of his subordinates.
    B. lead his followers out of a situation if danger is approaching.
    C. act without taking advice from his subordinates.
    D. realize his own limitations and delegate responsibilities to others.

__B__ 16. Which statement best expresses the theme of "Cupid's Arrows"?
p. 98,
TE p. 97

    A. Outward appearance is not as important as inward beauty.
    B. Love is more important than position and material possessions in the choice of
       a mate.
    C. Parents should do what is best for their children.
    D. There are times when a person should not try to do his or her best.

__B__ 17. In "The Progress of Poesy," Arnold's attitude toward aging is one of
pp. 100-1

    A. acceptance.
    B. despair.
    C. nonchalance.
    D. arrogance.

__A__ 18. Which conclusion do the authors of "On the Pleasures of No Longer Being Very
pp. 102-4   Young" and "The Soul's Dark Cottage" both share?

    A. Old age brings greater insight.
    B. Old age brings bitterness.
    C. Old age brings with it a loss of creativity.
    D. Old age enables one to view eternity better.

__B__ 19. An extended metaphor in which the characters, incidents, and situations have a meaning
p. 127   beyond the literal level of the narrative is called a/an

    A. symbol.
    B. allegory.
    C. analogy.
    D. fable.

__C__ 20. An allegorical story with two or more strictly correlated levels of meaning is called a/an
p. 128

    A. fable.
    B. analogy.
    C. parable.
    D. symbol.

__D__ 21. The seasonal metaphor in "The Ant and the Grasshopper" corresponds to
TE p. 131

    A. times of good weather and adverse weather.
    B. the changes that occur as a person ages.
    C. the ant's biological life cycle.
    D. times of prosperity and adversity.

B
pp. 4, 92, 144

22. Choose the literary device that does *not* appear in the following sentence referring to the Red Death: "He [the Red Death] had come like a thief in the night."

   A. simile
   B. synecdoche
   C. allusion
   D. personification

B
pp. 150-51

23. The terms *pun, foreshadowing,* and *understatement* all refer to types of

   A. dramatic irony.
   B. verbal irony.
   C. paradox.
   D. irony of situation.

B
pp. 154, 160-61

24. In both Wheelock's "Earth" and Frost's "A Considerable Speck (Microscopic),"

   A. the observers are human beings.
   B. the irony relates to human intelligence.
   C. those being observed are human beings.
   D. human intelligence is used wisely.

D
p. 162, TE p. 162

25. The hyperbole in "Scylla Toothless" is that

   A. Scylla has lost all her teeth.
   B. Scylla is extremely ugly.
   C. Scylla has grown old.
   D. Scylla's tongue has worn her teeth away.

B
p. 168

26. Which of the following actions from the opening paragraphs of "The Grave Grass Quivers" does *not* foreshadow the events to follow?

   A. The narrator's shovel strikes something.
   B. Doc Martindale says his father and brother were killed in 1861.
   C. Doc Martindale says, "Murdered."
   D. "We began to uncover things."

Short Answer

Write the word or phrase that best answers the question or defines the term.

27. To what does the term *metonymy* refer? ___an expression in which a related thing stands for the thing itself, p. 4___

28. What is synecdoche? ___an expression in which a part stands for the whole, p. 4___

29. What does the term *meter* mean? ___the arrangement of accented syllables that occur at fairly equal intervals, p. 26___

30. What are the units of meter called? ___poetic feet, p. 26___

31. What is the term for poetry that uses neither meter nor rhyme? ___free verse, p. 27___

32. What is an allusion? ___a reference within a written work to something outside it, p. 92___

MIDTERM

33. In "Cupid's Arrows" to what mythological goddess of the forest is Kitty compared, and why is this comparison an appropriate one? *Diana; both are skilled in archery. p. 96*

34. In "Eldorado" to what is the "pilgrim shadow" alluding in his reference to the "valley of the shadow"? *the "valley of the shadow of death" in the Twenty-third Psalm, p. 99, TE p. 100*

35. In "Pigeon Feathers" does David's observation of the patterns of the pigeons' feathers lead him to acceptance of Christ as his Savior? *no, pp. 122-23, TE p. 123*

36. Define the term *epigram*. *a short, highly compressed poem making a wise or humorous observation and ending with a witty twist, TE p. 130*

37. Define the term *fable*. *a story in which the details support the meaning collectively; may include a stated moral, p. 128, TE p. 139*

38. According to its literary definition, what does a *symbol* represent? *something in addition to itself, p. 126*

39. To what is the poet alluding in "Epigram" by his Biblical references to dust and to rainbows? *God's creation of man from dust and His covenant that man would never again be destroyed by a flood, p. 130*

40. In Keats's poem "The Grasshopper and the Cricket," the insects' songs are symbolic of what? *man's poetry, TE p. 132*

41. Discuss the specific situational irony in "A Special Occasion." *Situational irony occurs when the nurse judges the children's behavior based on her own adult perspective. pp. 156-58*

Matching I

Match each selection below with the allusion that appears in the selection.

     A. Cupid's Arrows
     B. The Donkey
     C. Eldorado
     D. On the Pleasures of No Longer Being Very Young
     E. Pigeon Feathers
     F. The Progress of Poesy
     G. The Soul's Dark Cottage

___**F**___ 42. Moses' smiting the rock to bring forth water
p. 100

___**G**___ 43. Moses' viewing the Promised Land from Mount Pisgah
TE p. 103

 E   44. *The Time Machine*
p. 106

 A   45. the Judgment of Paris
p. 97

 C   46. Psalm 23
p. 99

 B   47. Palm Sunday
p. 94

 D   48. Napoleon
p. 103

Matching II

Match the following selections with the correct themes or morals.

A. The Ant and the Grasshopper
B. Epigram
C. Fable
D. The Grasshopper and the Cricket
E. maggie and milly and molly and may
F. The Masque of the Red Death
G. My Star
H. The Nightingale and the Glowworm

 H   49. Both the aesthetic and didactic functions of poetry contribute to poetry's ability to make
p. 135   life more tolerable.

 D   50. Poetry is possible even in the winter, or the unpleasant circumstances, of life.
TE p. 132

 C   51. "Talents differ."
p. 136

 B   52. Without the presence of trials in life, one would not appreciate its joyful aspects.
p. 130

 G   53. Nearly everyone has some object or idea that fascinates him.
p. 145

 A   54. "It is thrifty to prepare today for the wants of tomorrow."
p. 131

 E   55. "For whatever we lose(like a you or a me) / it's always ourselves we find in the sea."
p. 137

 F   56. Death is inescapable.
p. 144

Matching III

Match the following terms with the correct definitions.

A. dramatic irony
B. foreshadowing
C. hyperbole
D. paradox
E. pun
F. sarcasm
G. satire
H. situational irony
I. structural irony
J. verbal irony

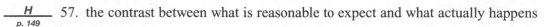

____H____ 57. the contrast between what is reasonable to expect and what actually happens
p. 149

____D____ 58. a seeming contradiction
p. 148

____E____ 59. the use of words identical in sound but different in meaning to create a double meaning
p. 151

____A____ 60. the contrast between a reader's knowledge and a character's ignorance
p. 149

____F____ 61. verbal irony that takes the form of mock praise
p. 150

____I____ 62. verbal irony that extends throughout an entire work
TE p. 153

____C____ 63. ironic overstatement
TE p. 162

____J____ 64. language that means something other than what it actually states
p. 150

____B____ 65. prophetic irony
p. 151

____G____ 66. corrective ridicule in literature
p. 151

Matching IV

Match the following works with their themes.

    A. At the Aquarium
    B. A Considerable Speck (Microscopic)
    C. Earth
    D. A Germ Destroyer
    E. The Golf Links Lie So Near the Mill
    F. The Grave Grass Quivers
    G. Letter from a West Texas Constituent
    H. Scylla Toothless
    I. A Special Occasion
    J. Yet If His Majesty, Our Sovereign Lord

____J____ 67. Man still makes no preparation for Christ's return.
p. 180

____I____ 68. Adults often misjudge childhood behavior because of an improper perspective.
p. 156

____C____ 69. Man's intelligence leads to his destruction.
p. 154

____B____ 70. An insect shows more intelligence than some writers.
p. 160

____G____ 71. A farmer shows the absurdity of government policy.
p. 159

____H____ 72. Gossip is detrimental to the one who gossips.
p. 162

____D____ 73. A person's reputation is ruined by an embarrassing mistake.
pp. 164-67

____A____ 74. Man shares a sense of aimlessness with nonhuman creatures.
p. 162

____F____ 75. A man's skill acquired from Indians reveals his guilt.
pp. 168-79

Multiple Choice

Choose the best answer from the choices given.

_____**B**_____
p. 182

1. Two major types of literature are poetry and

   A. fiction.
   B. prose.
   C. nonfiction.
   D. novels.

_____**A**_____
pp. 4, 190

2. Identify the imaginative comparison in the following excerpt from "The Day the Dam Broke": "The fact that we were all as safe as kittens under a cookstove did not assuage in the least the fine despair . . ."

   A. simile
   B. personification
   C. metaphor
   D. metonymy

_____**B**_____
p. 193

3. In "The Day the Dam Broke," Dr. Mallory mistakes what sound for rushing water?

   A. people rushing by him
   B. a boy rollerskating behind him
   C. people breathing
   D. a dog running at his heels

_____**D**_____
p. 194

4. In "A Slight Sound at Evening," White revisits an old vacation spot for each of the following reasons *except*

   A. to remember past days.
   B. to visit places he had been before.
   C. to fish.
   D. to visit an old friend he had not seen for years.

_____**D**_____
pp. 27, 196

5. In "A Slight Sound at Evening," White describes a noise as inducing "summer sleep." Here he is using

   A. assonance.
   B. consonance.
   C. onomatopoeia.
   D. alliteration.

_____**C**_____
pp. 196-97

6. Which is *not* a sound of the past in "A Slight Sound at Evening"?

   A. one camper greeting a new arrival
   B. a squirrel tapping on the roof
   C. an outboard motor
   D. a two-cylinder inboard motor

_____**A**_____
TE p. 199

7. The title "A Miserable Merry Christmas" can best be described as

   A. a paradox.
   B. onomatopoetic.
   C. an example of assonance.
   D. an example of consonance.

__B__
p. 199,
TE p. 199

8. Whose viewpoint dominates Steffens's account in "A Miserable Merry Christmas"?

   A. Steffens's father's
   B. Steffens's as a young boy
   C. Steffens's as an adult
   D. Steffens's mother's

__A__
p. 200

9. Which best describes the boy's father while he awaits the arrival of the pony in "A Miserable Merry Christmas"?

   A. He is worried and impatient.
   B. He is enjoying the humor of the situation.
   C. He believes that the wait would do the boy good.
   D. He becomes irritable with the children.

__D__
p. 205

10. Identify the imaginative comparison Welty uses in the following sentence from "Listening": "It had been startling and disappointing to me to find out that story books had been written by *people,* that books were not natural wonders, coming up of themselves like grass."

    A. personification
    B. metaphor
    C. synecdoche
    D. simile

__B__
pp. 204-6

11. According to "Listening," what was *not* a contribution of Eudora Welty's father to her life?

    A. curiosity
    B. wise use of money
    C. love for modern instruments
    D. appreciation for opera

__D__
pp. 4, 210

12. What imaginative comparison does Whittier use in the following statement from "Telling the Bees": "the same brook sings of a year ago"?

    A. metonymy
    B. simile
    C. metaphor
    D. personification

__D__
p. 211

13. In "Telling the Bees," what is the speaker's first deduction when he sees someone draping the beehives?

    A. The speaker's grandfather has died.
    B. The neighbor has died.
    C. His lover has died.
    D. His lover's grandfather has died.

__A__
pp. 4, 211

14. What imaginative comparison is the author of "Telling the Bees" using in the phrase "the slantwise rain / Of light through the leaves"?

    A. metaphor
    B. personification
    C. simile
    D. metonymy

TEST 7

<u>A</u> 15. In "Verifying One's References," how does Kipling react when his friend asks to verify
p. 213   what So-and-so has said?

- A. He is slightly upset.
- B. He is furious.
- C. He is equally curious.
- D. He is pleased.

<u>D</u> 16. According to "Life of Caesar," Caesar showed great fortitude by persevering in spite of
p. 215   all of the following physical problems *except* which one?

- A. a small body frame
- B. seizures from a related illness
- C. fair skin
- D. digestive problems

<u>A</u> 17. How is it that Pompey and Caesar lived peacefully ruling together?
p. 217

- A. They both were afraid of Crassus.
- B. Neither wanted to hurt Julia.
- C. They both knew this was best.
- D. They feared each other.

<u>B</u> 18. What happened the night before Caesar and Pompey went to battle?
p. 218

- A. A sacrifice was made.
- B. A flaming light landed in Pompey's camp.
- C. Pompey's forces panicked.
- D. A flaming light landed in Caesar's camp.

<u>C</u> 19. Caesar believed his plan to use javelins would be best because
p. 218

- A. javelins were very powerful.
- B. javelins were good to use at close distances.
- C. Pompey's young soldiers did not wish to have their faces injured.
- D. Pompey's men were not used to javelins.

<u>C</u> 20. Caesar feared Cassius because
p. 219

- A. Cassius's ancestor years earlier had killed a Roman king.
- B. Cassius was a friend of Brutus.
- C. Cassius was a thin, pale man.
- D. Cassius was powerful.

<u>B</u> 21. What did Caesar's will reveal?
p. 221

- A. his generosity to his friends
- B. his generosity to the Romans
- C. his generosity to his family
- D. his great wealth

<u>B</u> 22. In "Sir Francis Drake," the poet
p. 222

- A. wishes he could have sailed with Drake.
- B. is afraid there will be no more men like Drake.
- C. wishes he had met Drake.
- D. determines to accomplish great things like Drake.

Short Answer

Write the word or phrase that best answers the question or defines the term.

23. What does the term *genre* mean? <u>*a common type of literature, p. 182*</u>

24. What is a journal and how does it differ from a diary? <u>*A journal is a person's daily record of*</u>
<u>*happenings and impressions usually kept for a professional purpose; a diary also records daily hap-*</u>
<u>*penings and impressions, but is more intimate than a journal (not for professional purposes). p. 188*</u>

25. What do both the biography and the autobiography use to tell about an incident in a person's
life? <u>*an anecdote, p. 189*</u>

26. Give one example of irony from "The Day the Dam Broke." <u>*Answers may vary but might include*</u>
<u>*the title itself (because no dam breaks in the story); the way in which people jump to the conclusion*</u>
<u>*that something awful has occurred because "somebody began to run"; and the way in which the*</u>
<u>*narrator's mother carefully prepares for a nonexistent disaster. pp. 190-93*</u>

27. "Darius Conningway . . . was telling the Public Utilities Commission in the language of Julius
Caesar that they might as well try to move the Northern star as to move him." This quotation
from "The Day the Dam Broke" is an example of what literary device? <u>*an allusion, pp. 92, 190*</u>

28. Identify the following type of imaginative comparison from "A Slight Sound at Evening": "the
small steamboat that had a long rounded stern like the lip of a Ubangi . . ." <u>*simile (or allusion),*</u>
<u>*pp. 4, 92, 197*</u>

29. Give one example of situational irony in Steffens's essay "A Miserable Merry Christmas."
<u>*The boy repeatedly says that he wants nothing but a pony for Christmas, but when it appears that he*</u>
<u>*may indeed get "nothing," he reacts with dismay. TE p. 200*</u>

30. Give one example of dramatic irony in Steffens's essay "A Miserable Merry Christmas."
<u>*Despite the fact that the boy believes that he has received nothing for Christmas, the interaction be-*</u>
<u>*tween the father and mother on Christmas morning implies that there really is a pony coming. TE p. 200*</u>

31. According to "Listening," how did Welty benefit from a knowledge of time? <u>*It helped her learn*</u>
<u>*about chronology. p. 204*</u>

TEST 7

32. In "Listening" what was a favorite activity for Eudora and her mother? <u>for her mother to read</u> <u>to her, p. 205</u>

33. According to custom, what did one "tell the bees" and why? <u>about the death of a family member;</u> <u>to keep the bees from leaving the hives, p. 210</u>

34. Identify "journey" in the following lines: "For I knew she was telling the bees of one / Gone on the journey we all must go!" <u>death, p. 211</u>

35. According to "Verifying One's References," what is Kipling's philosophy about believing what one hears? <u>Everything should be checked before it is believed. p. 213</u>

36. Who put the life of Caesar in drama form? <u>William Shakespeare, p. 214</u>

37. What was the island that Caesar conquered that was "beyond the limits of the known world"? <u>Britain, p. 216</u>

38. What did Caesar do with the enemy soldiers after he defeated them? <u>pardoned them, p. 219</u>

39. Define "the Ides of March" mentioned in "Life of Caesar." <u>March 15, p. 220</u>

40. What allusion does Hayman use in "Sir Francis Drake" in reference to character traits being passed on? <u>a Biblical allusion to Elijah, p. 223</u>

41. Give at least one positive attribute that Caesar and Drake had in common. <u>Answers will vary.</u> <u>Ideas include bravery, a willingness to serve, personal greatness, wisdom, or leadership abilities. Allow</u> <u>any response that the students can support from details in the essay and poem. pp. 214-23</u>

Matching

Match the following terms with the correct definitions.

    A. anecdote
    B. autobiography
    C. biography
    D. comedy
    E. diary
    F. dramatic irony
    G. memoirs
    H. situational irony
    I. tragedy

<u>I</u> 42. play that ends unhappily
p. 184

<u>D</u> 43. play that ends happily
p. 185

TEST 7

C *p. 188*   44. history of a person's life

B *p. 188*   45. interpretation of an author's own life

E *p. 188*   46. personal record of the events in someone's life

G *p. 188*   47. a recollection of events from the author's public life

A *p. 189*   48. a special incident from the life of an important person

H *p. 149*   49. a contrast between what a character expects to happen and what actually happens

F *p. 149*   50. a contrast between what the reader knows and what a character in the story knows

Essay

In one or more paragraphs, completely answer *one* of the questions below, using examples from selections in this unit. You may use your own paper.

51a. Explain how Caesar would be a good role model or a poor role model.

> *Key ideas: Answers will vary. Good role model—Caesar was a kind man in that he showed pity on those*
>
> *he conquered, and he gave gifts to his own soldiers. He did not desire to amass wealth from those he*
>
> *conquered. He sought honor through being a courageous, faithful soldier. When poised between two*
>
> *enemies, he successfully defeated one of them, and then the other one surrendered. Even though he*
>
> *could have lived better than his troops, he chose to take journeys with them and sleep outside. He*
>
> *was a determined man. For example, in order to reach Germany, he built a bridge to cross the Rhine*
>
> *River, a first for any army. Poor role model—Caesar exhibited the characteristic of greed in his life.*
>
> *During a ten-year period, he took eight hundred towns and three hundred states. He also gave money*
>
> *to upcoming officials he wanted in office so that they could influence people to vote for them. Being*
>
> *a superstitious man, Caesar consulted seers and made sacrifices to gods. pp. 215-18.*

51b. What are two lessons the reader can learn from these different autobiographical and biographical excerpts?

> *Key ideas: Answers will vary; several examples follow. From "The Day the Dam Broke," the reader can*
>
> *learn not to believe everything he hears. A person should check the evidence of something before he*
>
> *believes it. Also, the reader can see that spreading unproven rumors can cause great confusion and*
>
> *trouble. In "A Slight Sound at Evening," the reader can see how family activities can make memories*
>
> *that last a lifetime and then can be shared with future generations. In the excerpt "Listening," the*

reader can learn how seemingly minor characteristics of a parent can have an effect on a child. For

example, Welty's father's interest in closely observing the weather gave her a sense of weather

occurrences in her own life and writing. Welty's mother impressed on her the importance of reading

as she read to her even at the age of two or three.

Multiple Choice

Choose the best answer from the choices given.

<u>**B**</u>
p. 239

1. In "The Sire de Maletroit's Door," why does the Sire insist that Denis marry Blanche even if he is not the young captain she met at church?

    A. He wants revenge.
    B. He wants to keep his family honor.
    C. He wants to be assured that Blanche will have a husband.
    D. He likes Denis.

<u>**A**</u>
p. 242

2. In "The Sire de Maletroit's Door," Denis says, "Life is a little vapor that passeth away." This statement is

    A. an allusion.
    B. ironic.
    C. symbolic.
    D. a simile.

<u>**A**</u>
TE pp.
249, 264

3. In "The Adventure of the Speckled Band," all of the following are reasons Watson makes a good narrator *except* that

    A. his medical knowledge adds to the accuracy of his reporting.
    B. he is easier for the reader to identify with than Holmes is.
    C. he lacks Holmes's deductive powers.
    D. he can narrate the story without disclosing the ending too early.

<u>**D**</u>
p. 263

4. In "The Adventure of the Speckled Band," what was the true purpose of the bell-rope by the bed?

    A. to call the servants
    B. no purpose
    C. to make someone think it could be used to call for servants
    D. to allow something to pass over it to the bed

<u>**D**</u>
pp. 27, 271

5. When Crane says "rear rank" and "still stretched" in "A Gray Sleeve" he is using

    A. metaphor.
    B. simile.
    C. personification.
    D. alliteration.

<u>**A**</u>
pp. 274–82

6. "A Gray Sleeve" and "Barbara Frietchie" are similar in each of the following ways *except* that

    A. they have Southern girls as protagonists.
    B. they are set during the Civil War.
    C. their conflict is a man versus a woman.
    D. they show human feelings.

<u>**A**</u>
TE p. 289

7. Which of the following proverbs states the lesson Hardy is teaching in "Tony Kytes, the Arch-Deceiver"?

    A. Liars do not prosper.
    B. You win some, you lose some.
    C. All is fair in love and war.
    D. Let sleeping dogs lie.

__B__   8. What is the primary kind of conflict in "Tony Kytes, the Arch-Deceiver"?
pp. 283-89

    A. man versus nature
    B. man versus himself
    C. man versus a force greater than himself
    D. none of the above

__A__   9. Tony Kytes's father tells Tony to marry the
p. 287

    A. girl who did not ask Tony for a ride.
    B. girl he loves.
    C. girl he proposed to first.
    D. kindest girl.

__A__   10. The speaker's tone in "The Listeners" is one of
pp. 290-91

    A. mystery.
    B. unhappiness.
    C. terror.
    D. admiration.

__C__   11. All of the following statements are true about "The Listeners" and "Foul Shot" *except*
pp. 290-93   which one?

    A. Both are narratives.
    B. Both withhold information from the audience.
    C. Both give a definite resolution.
    D. Both build in suspense.

__A__   12. What part of speech does Hoey use in "Foul Shot" to build suspense?
pp. 292-93

    A. verb
    B. adjective
    C. adverb
    D. noun

Short Answer

Write the word or phrase that best answers the question or defines the term.

13. What are the two modern fiction genres? *novel and short story, p. 226*

14. Define *fiction*. *an imagined story, p. 226*

15. Define *flashback*. *earlier events summarized as introductory background or inserted later parenthetically, pp. 226-27*

16. Define *dramatic irony*. *a situation in which a character (but not the reader) is surprised at the outcome, p. 227*

17. Define *external conflict*. *a struggle that takes place outside of the protagonist, p. 227*

18. Define *internal conflict*. *a struggle within the protagonist; man against himself, p. 227*

19. Define *flat character.* _a character who has little individuality, p. 228_

20. Define *developing character.* _a character who matures and changes, p. 228_

21. Define *round character.* _a character presented in great detail, p. 228_

22. Define *static character.* _a character who remains the same throughout a work, p. 228_

23. List two characteristics of Romantic fiction and tell how each is exemplified in "The Sire de Maletroit's Door." _Answers will vary but may include a distant time setting (1429); an emotionally turbulent atmosphere (two strangers locked in a bizarre house with death or marriage their only options); a distressed maiden (Blanche); a cruel antagonist (the Sire); a noble hero (Denis); and a climax culminating in emotion rather than reality (Denis and Blanche fall in love and agree to marry). pp. 230-44, TE pp. 230, 239, 244_

24. If the truth had been known about Lady Clare, who would have received an inheritance earlier? _Lord Ronald, pp. 245-46_

25. In "The Adventure of the Speckled Band," how does Holmes know Dr. Roylott has physically hurt Helen? _by the marks on her wrist, p. 254_

26. Name one incorrect conclusion Holmes draws in "The Speckled Band." _that the reference to a "band" was about the gypsies; that the metallic clang was the shutter lock dropping into place (either answer), pp. 255, 263_

27. In "The Adventure of the Speckled Band," what is the speckled band? _a swamp adder (snake), p. 263_

28. Which kind of conflict, external or internal, is foremost in "The Drummer Boy of Shiloh"? _internal, TE p. 265_

29. What are the two major symbols that Bradbury uses throughout the story "The Drummer Boy of Shiloh" and what do they represent? _the drum and the peach blossom (youth, innocence, and/or defenselessness), pp. 266, 268, TE pp. 266, 269_

30. How does Crane create a feeling of indecision in his writing? _by the use of words such as "might," "seem," and "maybe," TE p. 270_

31. What sound technique does Crane use when he says, "The innumerable hoofs thundered"?

    onomatopoeia, pp. 28, 271

32. What is one symbol that de la Mare uses in "The Listeners" and what does it represent? *(any*

    one of the three) the window (a mirror of the soul and ultimate reality), houses (death and ultimate

    reality), or the door (access to truth), TE p. 291

Matching I

Match the following terms with the correct definitions.

- A. antagonist
- B. atmosphere
- C. conflict
- D. flashback
- E. incident
- F. internal conflict
- G. plot
- H. protagonist
- I. setting
- J. tone

E
p. 226　　33. basic unit of a story

B
p. 228　　34. the prevalent emotion of a story

G
p. 227　　35. connected incidents

I
p. 228　　36. time and place

A
p. 228　　37. opponent

J
p. 228　　38. the author's attitude toward a character or situation

D
pp. 226-27　　39. summary of previous events

C
p. 227　　40. contending forces

H
p. 228　　41. main character

F
p. 227　　42. man versus himself

Matching II

Match each work with its theme or central idea.

   A. "Barbara Frietchie"
   B. "The Drummer Boy of Shiloh"
   C. "Foul Shot"
   D. "A Gray Sleeve"
   E. "Lady Clare"
   F. "The Listeners"
   G. "The Sire de Maletroit's Door"
   H. "Tony Kytes, the Arch-Deceiver"

F
 TE p. 291   43. Man cannot find truth in this world.

C
 p. 293   44. The author builds suspense by withholding the climax until the very end.

E
 pp. 245-47   45. True love is tested.

H
 pp. 283-89   46. An indecisive youth is swayed by feminine charm.

A
 p. 281   47. A woman is ready to die for what she believes.

D
 pp. 270-79   48. Vague hints can mislead someone.

G
 pp. 230-44   49. Romantic emotional incidents control the action.

B
 pp. 265-68   50. An older man inspires a youth who has an inner struggle.

Essay

In one or more paragraphs, completely answer *one* of the questions below, using examples from selections in this unit. You may use your own paper.

51a. Discuss either "The Listeners" or "Foul Shot," describing how each poet builds suspense.

Key ideas: Answers will vary. "The Listeners": The setting is night, with only one person out in the

forest knocking at the door of a house. The character tries to communicate with someone, but his

yelling is to no avail. The words de la Mare chooses also create suspense. Some examples are

"phantom listeners," "moonbeams on their dark stair," and "strangeness." pp. 290-91

"Foul Shot": Hoey tells the reader that the score is tied 60 to 60 and there are only two seconds left

on the clock for the game to be played. One of the players is on the foul line to try to make a shot.

Hoey goes into great detail to describe the player as he is standing at the foul line with the ball. He

uses an abundance of verbs: "seeks," "soothes," "drums," "measures," and others to create anticipa-

tion in the reader. Even the way Hoey shapes the last of the poem with single words attracts the reader's attention to read on to see what is going to happen. Finally, Hoey writes, "And then / And then / And then," and gives the resolution. pp. 292-93

51b. Discuss at least three different internal and/or external conflicts within works from this unit. Specify how that conflict is shown.

Key ideas: Answers will vary. In "The Adventure of the Speckled Band," Sherlock Holmes battles a human opponent, Grimesby Roylott, who is masterful in his strength and intelligence. In "The Sire de Maletroit's Door," Denis de Beaulieu's adversary is also a shrewd human, the Sire de Maletroit. Whittier in "Barbara Frietchie" shows the Union army against the Confederate army. Tony in "Tony Kytes, the Arch-Deceiver" experiences conflict with several young ladies and within himself. Besides external conflicts, there are internal conflicts such as the conflict that Bradbury's drummer boy faces with his own fears. Stephen Crane's protagonist, a Union infantry captain, battles with himself about his feelings for a Confederate young lady. pp. 230-44, 248-64, 265-68, 270-89

TEST 9

Name_____

Multiple Choice

Choose the best answer from the choices given.

<u>C</u>
TE p. 300

1. Wagoner uses all of the following to reinforce the meaning of his poem "March for a One-Man Band" *except*

   A. no rhyme.
   B. broken rhythm.
   C. clear punctuation.
   D. sound words.

<u>D</u>
pp. 27,
299-300

2. In "March for a One-Man Band," Wagoner's words *boom, toot,* and *sloop* show the poet's use of

   A. alliteration.
   B. onomatopoeia.
   C. consonance.
   D. assonance.

<u>A</u>
pp. 301-2

3. In "Who Has Seen the Wind?" the only assumption the author does *not* make about the wind is that

   A. the wind is calming.
   B. one cannot see the wind.
   C. the wind has power.
   D. the movement of objects shows the presence of the wind.

<u>D</u>
TE p. 302

4. In "Who Has Seen the Wind?" Rossetti is showing that

   A. one must see something to prove its existence.
   B. no one can be sure of the existence of the wind.
   C. the wind destroys.
   D. sight is not the only way one can be sure the wind exists.

<u>C</u>
TE p. 305

5. The windows in the poem "The Windows" are probably the

   A. windows of heaven.
   B. windows of Herbert's country home.
   C. stained glass windows in a cathedral.
   D. windows in the temple at Jerusalem.

<u>D</u>
TE p. 305

6. In "The Windows" placing the glass into a fire is compared to

   A. breaking the Christian's will.
   B. taking a stand for Christ.
   C. having the power of God in one's life.
   D. maintaining a testimony even in trials.

<u>A</u>
p. 305

7. The metaphor Herbert uses for doctrine in "The Windows" is

   A. the light.
   B. life.
   C. the colors in the window.
   D. the glass of the window.

B
TE p. 306

8. "High Flight" was first published

    A. during World War I.
    B. during World War II.
    C. after World War II.
    D. during the 1950s.

C
pp. 27, 307

9. In "High Flight" when Magee refers to the clouds as "sun-split," he is using

    A. assonance.
    B. consonance.
    C. alliteration.
    D. onomatopoeia.

D
pp. 4, 307,
TE p. 307

10. The reference in "High Flight" to "shouting wind" is an example of

    A. alliteration.
    B. metaphor.
    C. simile.
    D. personification.

D
p. 308

11. According to Hillyer's "The Wise Old Apple Tree in Spring," how does the orchard keeper identify which trees he is going to cut down?

    A. He puts a ribbon around them.
    B. He puts a mark of paint on the side of them.
    C. He puts a metal band around them.
    D. He puts a mark of chalk on them.

D
p. 308,
TE p. 309

12. Who would Hillyer say are the "orchard men of time"?

    A. poets
    B. men who prune fruit trees
    C. men who appreciate beauty
    D. men who value only those things that produce instant gratification

D
pp. 4, 310

13. When the author of "Traveling Through the Dark" speaks of the wilderness listening, he is using

    A. a metaphor.
    B. a simile.
    C. consonance.
    D. personification.

C
pp. 28, 310

14. In "Traveling Through the Dark," the "hood purred" is an example of

    A. alliteration.
    B. assonance.
    C. onomatopoeia.
    D. metaphor.

D
p. 312

15. In "Dust of Snow," what shakes snow on the speaker?

    A. a raven
    B. a blue jay
    C. a robin
    D. a crow

___C___ 16. What pictures does the author present of the dog in "The Span of Life"?
p. 312

    A. present and future
    B. present, past, and future
    C. present and past
    D. past and future

___A___ 17. What is the theme of "Dust of Snow"?
p. 312,
TE p. 313

    A. A small event in nature may change someone's outlook.
    B. Nature is a gift from God to be appreciated.
    C. Winter gives pleasure to people.
    D. Winter may change people's moods.

Short Answer

Write the word or phrase that best answers the question.

18. List three characteristics of lyric poetry. _emotion, poet gives his own thoughts, personal experience,_

    _p. 296_

19. List at least one way in which a lyric poem is similar to a soliloquy. _(Accept any one of the_

    following ideas.) In a soliloquy and in lyric poetry, the author gives his own thoughts to an audience.

    Just as an actor gives a speech on the stage, the author gives his "speech" in a poem to his audience,

    the reader. The actor speaks of personal experience, and so does the writer of the poem. The lyric

    poem also has props, costumes, and scenery as a drama does, but in the case of the poem, these

    items are in the audience's imagination. p. 296

20. Give two examples of Chávez's use of sound and images in "Rattlesnake." _sound: alliteration_

    ("crawl-created," "coil of cloisonné"); assonance (line, alive, by, diamond, like, hive; stay, away, created,

    articulated, cloisonné); rhyme (alive, hive; sand, band; stay, away, cloisonné; created, articulated);

    consonance (/d/); images: "Line of beauty," "by God's finger," "diamond-patterned inlaid band,"

    "cloisonné," "scrawled alive," "scrolling inward like a hive," "crawl-created, / articulated / coil," p. 297,

    _TE p. 298_

21. Wagoner's use of the words "tweedledy" and "bumbledy" in "March for a One-Man Band"
    exemplifies what? _rhyme or onomatopoeia, pp. 27-28, 299_

22. When the "trees bow down" in "Who Has Seen the Wind?" what is this a spiritual reference to?
    one bowing down in worship, TE p. 303

23. When the author of "Who Has Seen the Wind?" says the "trees bow down their heads," what kind of imaginative comparison is she using, aside from allusion? *personification, pp. 4, 302*

24. What kind of imaginative comparison does Herbert use to develop his poem "The Windows"? *a metaphor, pp. 4, 305, TE p. 305*

25. In the last stanza of "The Windows," what represents life (Christ within the preacher)? *the colors of the stained glass, p. 305*

26. What does the word *crazy* in line 2 of "The Windows" actually mean? *crazed or cracked, p. 305*

27. What is the message or theme of "The Windows"? *that the more suffering one endures the more radiant his testimony will be for Christ, TE p. 305*

28. Magee uses some onomatopoetic words in "High Flight." These words are not as obvious in this poem as in some other poems, but they still are examples of onomatopoeia. Give two examples from "High Flight." *any two of the following: "slipped," "soared," "flung," "swung," "trod," p. 307, TE p. 308*

29. In "The Wise Old Apple Tree in Spring," what does the apple tree represent? *the beauty in life that, though it does not produce anything useful, is good in and of itself, p. 308*

30. Why does the author not want "The Wise Old Apple Tree" cut down? *He enjoys the beautiful blossoms of the tree. p. 308*

31. In "Traveling Through the Dark," why does the speaker think it is necessary to move the deer? *Another car may swerve to miss the deer and in the process cause another accident in which people are killed. p. 310*

32. What does the speaker realize when he touches the deer in "Traveling Through the Dark"? *that the fawn inside her is living, p. 310*

33. What word occurs at the beginning and end of "Traveling Through the Dark" to heighten the sense of this dilemma? *"edge," p. 310, TE p. 311*

34. What two "swervings" does the author speak of in "Traveling Through the Dark"? *the swerving of a car and his swerving from his decision, p. 310, TE p. 311*

35. Who is the author of "Dust of Snow" and "The Span of Life"? *Robert Frost, pp. 312-13*

36. In "The Span of Life," why does the dog "bark backwards"? *He is old and does not want to get up. p. 313*

Matching I

Match the following imaginative comparisons with the correct examples. Answers may be used more than once or not at all.

    A. metaphor
    B. metonymy
    C. personification
    D. simile
    E. synecdoche

D 37. "scrolling inward like a hive"
pp. 4, 297

A 38. "coil of cloisonné"
pp. 4, 297

C 39. "I could hear the wilderness listen."
pp. 4, 310

E 40. "Has given my heart / A change of mood"
pp. 4, 312

A 41. "He is a brittle, crazy glass"
pp. 4, 305

C 42. "How spring . . . defeats the orchard men of time."
pp. 4, 308

Matching II

Match each selection with its theme or central idea.

    A. "Dust of Snow"   E. "Traveling Through the Dark"
    B. "High Flight"   F. "Who Has Seen the Wind?"
    C. "March for a One-Man Band"   G. "The Windows"
    D. "Rattlesnake"   H. "The Wise Old Apple Tree in Spring"

H 43. The beauty of something is as important as practical use.
pp. 308-9, TE pp. 308-9

B 44. Nature reflects the glory of "the face of God."
pp. 306-7, TE pp. 306-7

F 45. One's inability to see something does not mean that the thing does not exist.
pp. 301-2, TE p. 303

A 46. The beauty of nature may encourage someone to make the best of a situation.
p. 312, TE pp. 312-13

E 47. The speaker confronts a moral problem.
p. 310, TE p. 310

G 48. This metaphoric poem compares a preacher to an inanimate object.
p. 305, TE pp. 304-5

D 49. This poem gives the poet's image of and response to an animal.
p. 297

C 50. This poem emphasizes sound and syntax over rhyme.
p. 299, TE p. 300

Essay

In one or more paragraphs, completely answer *one* of the questions below, using examples from selections in this unit. You may use your own paper.

51a. Identify Herbert's metaphor in "The Windows" and explain his development of this metaphor.

> *Key ideas: The poet first uses the metaphor to illustrate man's weakness in lines 1 and 2. Man's inner nature is brittle like glass, and thus able to be cracked. This wordplay here also implies man's penchant not only for weakness (being cracked) but also for being irrational (crazed). The poet goes on to focus on the place wherein the glass is "housed." A stained glass window is usually housed in a magnificent cathedral. So too we, though cracked and brittle, are afforded a place in God's house. This stanza also points to why we are housed in God's sacred edifice. Like the stained glass windows in a cathedral, we are permitted to "enhance by color and light" God's rich grace. Stanza 2 points to the fact that the hotter the furnace that prepares the glass, the brighter the colors produced. So too the greater the suffering, the brighter the testimony of those who bear witness of Christ. Stanza 3 brings the metaphor to a climax, combining the ideas and images presented in the first two stanzas. TE p. 305.*

51b. Lyric poetry presents different human emotions. Discuss some of the emotions in the poems in the unit.

> *Key ideas: In "Rattlesnake" Chávez admires the beautiful snake God has created but also responds to the danger it poses. "March for a One-Man Band" elaborates on the pleasure the author experiences from hearing one man perform on many instruments. Pleasure and delight are also the emotions expressed by John Gillespie Magee, Jr., in "High Flight" as he zooms into the sky. Christina Rossetti in "Who Has Seen the Wind?" and Robert Hillyer in "The Wise Old Apple Tree in Spring" show an appreciation of God's creation. William Stafford in "Traveling Through the Dark" demonstrates a reverence for wildlife. pp. 297-303, 306-11*

51c. How do form, rhythm, and sound enhance meaning in "Dust of Snow" and "The Span of Life"?

> *Key ideas: Both poems are compact, expressing only one idea in each poem. Frost writes "Dust of Snow" in only one sentence, but he divides the sentence into two four-line stanzas. The poet uses the short iambic dimeter foot. The first stanza tells what the crow does, and the second stanza tells Frost's reaction to the crow's dusting of snow. In the first line of "The Span of Life," the pacing is*

reminiscent of a dog barking. The rhythm of line 2 causes the line to bounce along like a pup. The

first line speaks of the tiredness of the old dog—that everything is more of a struggle now. The sec-

ond line evokes a feeling of melancholy nostalgia. pp. 312-13, TE pp. 312-13

Multiple Choice

Choose the best answer from the choices given.

___B___
p. 320

1. Each of the following statements is true about Shakespeare *except*

    A. he was born in Stratford, England.
    B. he received an average education.
    C. he acted with a group in London.
    D. he wrote about two plays a year.

___B___
p. 320

2. The grammar Shakespeare studied was

    A. English.
    B. Latin.
    C. Roman.
    D. Italian.

___B___
p. 323

3. *Romeo and Juliet* occurs during the

    A. 1200s.
    B. 1300s.
    C. 1400s.
    D. 1500s.

___B___
TE p. 333

4. What is the first coincidence that occurs in *Romeo and Juliet* (Act I, Scene ii)?

    A. Romeo sees Capulet's guest list.
    B. Capulet's servant cannot read.
    C. Romeo's friend is invited to the Capulet feast.
    D. Romeo's name is on the guest list.

___C___
TE p. 338

5. In Act I what theme is introduced as Romeo states, "I fear too early, for my mind misgives / Some consequence yet hanging in the stars"?

    A. astronomy theme
    B. consequence theme
    C. fate theme
    D. death theme

___C___
TE p. 351

6. What is unique about Juliet's soliloquy in Act II, Scene ii?

    A. It is the shortest soliloquy in the play.
    B. It is the first of ten soliloquies in the play.
    C. It is overheard.
    D. It is the longest soliloquy in the play.

___C___
p. 361

7. In Act II Friar Lawrence is happy about Romeo and Juliet's relationship because

    A. now Romeo will be happy.
    B. Rosaline was unfit for Romeo.
    C. now the feuding may end.
    D. he knows the two truly love each other.

<u>**B**</u>
p. 372

8. In Act III which suggestion is made by Benvolio concerning the argument between Tybalt and Mercutio?

   A. Discuss things in public.
   B. Leave and try to talk out your problems.
   C. Fight in public.
   D. Fight in a private place.

<u>**A**</u>
TE p. 371

9. Shakespeare indicates that Mercutio and Tybalt both died because

   A. of their own actions.
   B. of fate.
   C. others encouraged them to fight.
   D. they were eager to prove themselves good swordsmen.

<u>**C**</u>
pp. 373-74

10. Romeo tries to stop the fight between Tybalt and Mercutio in Act III by doing all of the following *except*

    A. asking Mercutio to put away his sword.
    B. reminding them of what the Prince said about fighting in the street.
    C. asking them to talk together.
    D. physically coming between the two men.

<u>**D**</u>
p. 378

11. In Act III, after Tybalt's death, the Prince decrees that Romeo

    A. must be imprisoned.
    B. must be hanged.
    C. must have nothing to do with any Capulet.
    D. must never return to the city.

<u>**D**</u>
p. 380

12. As the Nurse comes in to Juliet in Act III, Scene ii, Juliet first assumes that

    A. Tybalt is dead.
    B. Tybalt killed Romeo.
    C. Romeo killed Tybalt.
    D. Romeo is dead.

<u>**A**</u>
p. 388

13. In Act III Friar Lawrence gives several reasons Romeo should be happy. Which one is *not* a reason the Friar gives?

    A. Juliet loves him.
    B. Tybalt did not kill him.
    C. Juliet is alive.
    D. He is exiled.

<u>**C**</u>
pp. 395, 397

14. When Juliet refuses to marry Paris (Act III), her parents react in all the following ways *except* which one?

    A. One wishes Juliet had never been born.
    B. One wishes she were dead.
    C. They think she is not in her right mind.
    D. They think she is proud.

<u>**D**</u>
p. 400

15. In Act IV why does Paris believe Capulet wants him to marry Juliet in such haste?

    A. Juliet desires this.
    B. Her father is afraid she will marry Romeo.
    C. Her father is afraid Juliet will run away.
    D. Her father believes Paris will help console Juliet.

A
p. 406

16. When Juliet returns home after talking to Friar Lawrence in Act IV, she does each of the following *except*

   A. give her father a kiss.
   B. tell her father she has been to Friar Lawrence's.
   C. tell her father she will marry Paris.
   D. ask her father's forgiveness.

B
pp. 408-9

17. Which is *not* a thought of Juliet's as she prepares to take the potion?

   A. The priest may really want her to die.
   B. Someone may realize she is not dead.
   C. The potion may not work.
   D. She may awaken and be alone in the vault.

D
p. 418

18. Romeo appeals to the Apothecary with all of the following reasons *except* which one?

   A. He looks like he is starving.
   B. The law is not a friend of his.
   C. He is going to have to beg for a living.
   D. His children will have nothing.

C
p. 420

19. Friar John did not succeed in his errand because

   A. he became ill.
   B. he had to help someone who was ill.
   C. officials quarantined the house where he was.
   D. Romeo was quarantined in a house.

D
p. 423,
TE p. 421

20. Which fact is *not* true of Paris?

   A. He persists in his love for Juliet.
   B. He believes Romeo has come to hurt Tybalt's body.
   C. He does not know of Romeo's love for Juliet.
   D. He wants to die since Juliet is dead.

Short Answer

Write the word or phrase that best answers the question.

21. How did the Elizabethan stage producer show different actions at the same time? __by the use of__

    balconies, p. 317

22. All of the action in Act I takes place on what day? __Sunday, pp. 324-48__

23. What does Juliet mean when in Act I she says, "My only love sprung from my only hate"?

    A person from a hated family is now the one she loves. p. 348

24. What is ironic about Mercutio's accusing Benvolio of being quick tempered (Act III)?

    Mercutio himself is the one who is quick tempered. TE p. 371

25. What is ironic about Romeo's effort to stop the fighting between Tybalt and Mercutio in Act III?

    In Romeo's effort to be peaceful, his friend ends up being killed. p. 375

26. Why does Capulet change the wedding plans (Act IV)? *He is surprised that Juliet has changed in her feelings, and he does not want her to back out of the wedding. p. 407*

27. What mood does Shakespeare present in Act IV, Scene v, as Juliet's "death" is discovered, and why does he do this? *humorous, because the audience already knows the truth about her, TE p. 411*

28. On what day does Act V take place? *Thursday, p. 416*

29. What, according to Romeo, is the irony of the Apothecary's exchanging poison for gold (Act V)? *Romeo says the gold is "worse poison" than the poison itself. p. 418*

30. What is Friar Lawrence's suggestion to Juliet in the final scene? *to go to a nunnery, p. 428*

True/False

If the statement is completely true, write *true*. If any part of the statement is false, write *false*.

true
p. 316
31. With the Elizabethan stage, the actor and audience were closer to each other than they are today.

true
p. 318
32. *Romeo and Juliet* considers various choices that young people must make.

true
pp. 318-19
33. Shakespeare shows Romeo and Juliet in a respectable relationship.

false
p. 333,
TE p. 333
34. When Capulet says (Act I, Scene ii), "'Tis not hard, I think, / For men so old as we to keep the peace," he is showing his desire for this feud to continue.

true
p. 333
35. Juliet is thirteen years old.

false
p. 370, TE p. 368
36. Romeo and Juliet are married on-stage in Act II.

true
TE p. 391
37. In Act III, Scene v, the lark represents the day and the nightingale evening.

true
p. 399
38. After marrying Romeo, Juliet does not appreciate the Nurse's advice about what she should do in her predicament with Romeo and Paris (Act III).

false
p. 428
39. Juliet kills herself by kissing Romeo who has the poison on his lips and by drinking the last of the poison that he has.

true
p. 432
40. The Prince blames the hatred between the Capulets and the Montagues for the deaths of these young people.

true
p. 432
41. The Prince takes some blame for what has happened with so many deaths.

Matching

Match the following terms with the best examples from *Romeo and Juliet.*

A. alliteration   F. oxymoron
B. Biblical allusion   G. simile
C. classical allusion   H. synecdoche
D. foreshadowing   I. personification
E. metaphor

___E___ 42. "Love is a smoke."
pp. 4, 331

___B___ 43. ". . . of nothing first created!"
pp. 92, 330

___H___ 44. "Let two more summers wither . . . "
pp. 4, 333

___I___ 45. "Earth hath swallowed up all my hopes but she."
pp. 4, 333

___G___ 46. Juliet is "As a rich jewel in an Ethiop's ear."
pp. 4, 344

___A___ 47. "madman's mercy"
pp. 27, 424

___F___ 48. "Feather of lead, bright smoke, cold fire, sick health"
p. 330, TE pp. 324, 330

___C___ 49. "Titan's fiery wheels"
pp. 92, 359

___D___ 50. "Methinks I see thee now, thou art so low, / As one dead in the bottom of a tomb."
pp. 151, 393

Essay

In one or more paragraphs, completely answer *one* **of the questions below, using examples from selections in this unit. You may use your own paper.**

51a. *Romeo and Juliet* opens with the Chorus introducing the theme of fate by referring to Romeo and Juliet as "a pair of star-cross'd lovers." Nevertheless, man's free will actually predominates through the drama. Give at least three examples in which decisions that characters make of their own free will affect the plot.

Key ideas: Examples are quite numerous. Romeo and his friends choose to "crash" Capulet's party;

had they not done so, he would not have met Juliet. Romeo decides to get revenge on Tybalt; had he

chosen otherwise, he would not have been banished. Juliet chooses to lie to her parents about her

willingness to marry Paris; had she told the truth, her life and Romeo's would have been spared.

Capulet moves up the date of Juliet's wedding to Paris; had he not done so, the outcome of the play

might have been quite different.

TEST 10

51b. Shakespearean tragedies include heroic protagonists who suffer because of a tragic flaw—a weakness that causes their downfall—in their character. What is Romeo and Juliet's tragic flaw? Give examples of the flaw and the tragic results of it.

Key ideas: Romeo and Juliet's tragic flaw is haste. Examples include Romeo's impetuous switch from

Rosaline to Juliet; their hasty wedding; the lovers' rash decisions to commit suicide; and the time

frame of the play.

Multiple Choice

Choose the best answer from the choices given.

__C__
p. 438

1. In preparation for the vault jump ("Crossing the Bar on a Fiberglas Pole"), Dubber does all the following *except*

   A. try to mentally prepare himself.
   B. see how many steps are before the bar.
   C. respond to the cheering crowds.
   D. try to loosen his body.

__D__
p. 438

2. As Dubber jogs down the runway, he hears

   A. his own footsteps.
   B. his lungs pumping.
   C. the crowd.
   D. his heart beating.

__C__
pp. 4, 27, 438

3. What type of imaginative comparison and what type of sound device does Dubber use as he says, "My hands and fingers clench the pole like wrenches"?

   A. metonymy, alliteration
   B. personification, synecdoche
   C. simile, consonance
   D. synecdoche, metaphor

__C__
TE p. 448

4. What is Helen Keller's purpose in "Three Days to See"?

   A. to reveal the tragedy of being blind
   B. to describe in detail things she can only imagine
   C. to encourage people to appreciate their senses
   D. to express gratitude to Anne Sullivan for being her "eyes"

__B__
p. 441

5. According to Keller, how much does a sighted person actually see?

   A. nothing
   B. a little
   C. almost as much as the blind
   D. everything around

__A__
pp. 4, 441

6. Keller's statement that her "heart cries" is an example of

   A. personification.
   B. metonymy.
   C. simile.
   D. assonance.

__D__
p. 442

7. What or who would be the first thing that Helen Keller would want to see on her first day?

   A. nature
   B. her home surroundings
   C. a close friend
   D. her teacher

C
p. 443

8. Helen Keller uses all of the following illustrations *except* which one to show how people do not observe accurately?

   A. A husband does not know the color of his wife's eyes.
   B. People do not observe the inner nature of a person by what they see at first.
   C. People cannot describe the inside of a friend's home.
   D. Few eyewitnesses of something even out of the ordinary see details.

C
p. 448

9. Keller considers closing her imaginary third day by

   A. visiting a close friend.
   B. watching nature.
   C. attending a humorous play.
   D. walking down Park Avenue.

B
p. 450

10. According to "How to Get Things Done," what does Benchley do as soon as he has eaten breakfast?

    A. makes his list of what to do
    B. goes back to bed
    C. starts his first task
    D. decides what to put on his list of things to do

A
p. 450

11. Which of the following does Benchley *not* plan to do during the week?

    A. write a short story
    B. cut out magazine articles
    C. answer letters
    D. get a haircut

D
p. 450

12. Benchley's reference to Juvenal *("Mens sana in corpore sano")* is an example of

    A. Biblical allusion.
    B. exaggeration.
    C. irony.
    D. classical allusion.

C
pp. 451-52

13. Benchley is constantly being distracted from his writing by

    A. what he hears.
    B. an idea he has.
    C. something he sees.
    D. an easier task.

B
p. 454

14. Hardison's opening anecdote in "On the Road Again with Recorded Books" accomplishes all of the following *except*

    A. setting the stage for the central point of the essay.
    B. illustrating the similarities between the author's and his son's listening tastes.
    C. reinforcing the author's concluding comment.
    D. serving to spark the reader's interest.

B
p. 456

15. Which statement is *not* true about Hardison after his first experience of listening to recorded books while traveling?

    A. He determines that he will take another book on his next trip.
    B. He believes that everyone should enjoy David Howarth's *Year of the Conquest*.
    C. Driving is more pleasurable now.
    D. He no longer minds taking a longer route to his destination.

_____A_____ 16. In "A Piece of Chalk," Chesterton asks the lady who owns the house for
p. 457

     A. brown paper.
     B. writing paper.
     C. a notepad.
     D. some scrap paper.

_____C_____ 17. What figure of sound does Chesterton use when he says the "first fierce stars"?
p. 457

     A. consonance
     B. onomatopoeia
     C. alliteration
     D. assonance

_____D_____ 18. Chesterton's use of the words "primal twilight of the first toil" shows
pp. 27, 457

     A. assonance, consonance, and onomatopoeia.
     B. consonance, onomatopoeia, and alliteration.
     C. assonance, alliteration, and onomatopoeia.
     D. assonance, alliteration, and consonance.

_____C_____ 19. Chesterton originally goes out to sketch
p. 458

     A. cows.
     B. the sunrise.
     C. saints and seraphim.
     D. the surrounding land.

_____B_____ 20. Which sense does Chesterton appeal to the most in "A Piece of Chalk"?
pp. 457-59

     A. touch
     B. sight
     C. hearing
     D. taste

Short Answer

Write the word or phrase that best answers the question or completes the phrase.

21. How is the personal essay similar to a letter? _The style of the personal essay is usually relaxed._

     The essay is addressed to an individual—the reader. The writer takes the reader into his confidence.

     He shares his personal experiences and thoughts with the reader. p. 436

22. What are two purposes of the personal essay? _to entertain and to teach, p. 436_

23. Dubber compares his fiberglass pole to what? Be specific. _a monster, pp. 438-39_

24. As Dubber falls into a "soft white mass," what is the best sight that he sees? _a crossbar still in_

     place, p. 439

25. What reason does Benchley give for reading the newspaper? _There might be something in the_

     paper about snake charming. p. 452

26. What is ironic about the title of Benchley's essay? *He actually accomplishes very little of any*

importance. pp. 149, 450-52

27. List several benefits of recorded books. *They help pass time that might otherwise be tedious; they*

afford opportunities for learning new things; they can introduce you to many good literary works.

p. 454

28. Briefly describe the style of Hardison's essay. *The style might be called "chatty" or "homespun."*

It has an informal, flowing style. TE p. 454

29. According to Chesterton, what is the "infant of the sword"? *pocketknife, p. 457*

30. What imaginative comparison does Chesterton use when he says the "landscape was as kindly as

any of its cottages"? *simile, pp. 4, 457*

31. Chesterton compares the color white to several aspects of Christianity. What are two of these

aspects? *virtue, mercy, chastity (any two), p. 458*

32. What is the final irony in Chesterton's essay? *He is angry at himself for forgetting white chalk*

until he realizes he is sitting on a "warehouse of white chalk." p. 459

Matching I

Match the following works with the correct subject matter or theme. Selections may be used more than once.

 A "Crossing the Bar on a Fiberglas Pole"
 B. "How to Get Things Done"
 C. "On the Road Again with Recorded Books"
 D. "A Piece of Chalk"
 E. "Three Days to See"

__B__ 33. procrastination
pp. 450-53

__E__ 34. careful use of senses
pp. 440-48

__A__ 35. a step-by-step description of a process
pp. 437-39

__D__ 36. a comparison of color and Christianity
pp. 457-59

__C__ 37. a method for making time pass quickly
pp. 454-56

__A__ 38. facing a test with success
pp. 437-39

__B__ 39. a parody
pp. 450-53

__D__ 40. a boyhood experience symbolizing a moral truth
pp. 457-59

TEST 11

Matching II

Match the following terms with the correct examples of the terms.

A. alliteration
B. allusion
C. assonance
D. consonance
E. irony

F. metaphor
G. onomatopoeia
H. personification
I. simile
J. symbol

___G___ 41. "I smack the pavement . . . "
p. 438

___C___ 42. "peat streams of the North"
p. 457

___A___ 43. "I *s*tared *s*tupidly *r*ound, *r*acking my brain for expedients."
p. 459

___H___ 44. "Silence would teach him the joys of sound."
p. 441

___D___ 45. "bearing nail*s*, bracket*s*, the evening paper*s*, and some cracker*s*"
p. 452

___J___ 46. "I suppose every one must have reflected how primeval and how poetical are the things that one carries in one's pocket."
p. 457

___E___ 47. "A great many people have come up to me and asked me how I manage to get so much work done and still keep looking so dissipated."
p. 450

___I___ 48. "The lifting of the whole land was like the lifting of one enormous wave to wash them all away."
p. 458

___F___ 49. "The narrators are usually pretty good, but there are rotten apples in every barrel."
p. 454

___B___ 50. "This, I think, is the mistake that people make about old poets who lived before Wordsworth."
p. 458

Essay

In one or more paragraphs, completely answer *one* of the questions below, using examples from selections in this unit. You may use your own paper.

51a. Explain how a personal essay is similar to a lyric poem. Prove this by using specific examples from one work.

Key ideas: Answers will vary. "Crossing the Bar on a Fiberglas Pole" is similar to a lyric poem. A lyric

poem gives a personal view just as David Dubber gives his personal view of what it is like to pole-

vault. A lyric poem also relates what the author thinks as does Dubber's essay. In the essay, the reader

finds out exactly what Dubber is thinking as he is running, jumping, and going over the bar. A lyric

poem gives description, and Dubber describes in detail the process of pole-vaulting. Finally, just as a

lyric poem is entertaining and purposeful, so is Dubber's essay. Dubber's "blow by blow" account, plus his usage of picturesque words at certain places such as his description of the pole being alive, make

the essay fascinating. Dubber also has a purpose—it is not the pole but the vaulter that determines

the success of a jump. pp. 437-39

51b. Discuss at least three different examples of Chesterton's symbolic use of color.

Key ideas: Chesterton associates the quality of brownness with the fall woods, the peat streams, and

the creation. Chesterton explains that white is a color, not the absence of color. It is "a shining affirm-

ative thing, as fierce as red, as definite as black." TE, pp. 457-58

FINAL

Name_____

Multiple Choice

Choose the best answer from the choices given.

__B__
p. 182

1. Two major types of literature are poetry and

    A. fiction.
    B. prose.
    C. nonfiction.
    D. novels.

__A__
TE p. 199

2. The title "A Miserable Merry Christmas" can best be described as

    A. a paradox.
    B. onomatopoetic.
    C. an example of assonance.
    D. an example of consonance.

__D__
p. 215

3. According to "Life of Caesar," Caesar showed great fortitude by persevering in spite of all of the following physical problems *except* which one?

    A. a small body frame
    B. seizures from a related illness
    C. fair skin
    D. digestive problems

__A__
p. 242

4. In "The Sire de Maletroit's Door," Denis says, "Life is a little vapor that passeth away." This statement is

    A. an allusion.
    B. ironic.
    C. symbolic.
    D. a simile.

__C__
pp. 290-93

5. All of the following statements are true about "The Listeners" and "Foul Shot" *except* which one?

    A. Both are narratives.
    B. Both at some point withhold information from the audience.
    C. Both give a definite resolution.
    D. Both build in suspense.

__D__
TE p. 302

6. In "Who Has Seen the Wind?" Rossetti is showing that

    A. one must see something to prove its existence.
    B. no one can be sure of the existence of the wind.
    C. the wind destroys.
    D. sight is not the only way one can be sure the wind exists.

__D__
TE p. 305

7. In "The Windows" placing the glass into a fire is compared to

    A. breaking the Christian's will.
    B. taking a stand for Christ.
    C. having the power of God in one's life.
    D. maintaining a testimony even in trials.

<u>**D**</u>
<small>p. 308,
TE p. 309</small>

8. According to "The Wise Old Apple Tree in Spring," who would Hillyer say are the "orchard men of time"?

 A. poets
 B. men who prune fruit trees
 C. men who appreciate beauty
 D. men who value only those things that produce instant gratification

<u>**C**</u>
<small>p. 313</small>

9. What pictures does the author present of the dog in "The Span of Life"?

 A. present and future
 B. present, past, and future
 C. present and past
 D. past and future

<u>**A**</u>
<small>p. 312,
TE p. 313</small>

10. What is the theme of "Dust of Snow"?

 A. A small event in nature may change someone's outlook.
 B. Nature is a gift from God to be appreciated.
 C. Winter gives pleasure to people.
 D. Winter may change people's moods.

<u>**C**</u>
<small>TE p. 338</small>

11. In Act I of *Romeo and Juliet,* what theme is introduced as Romeo states, "I fear too early, for my mind misgives / Some consequence yet hanging in the stars"?

 A. astronomy theme
 B. consequence theme
 C. fate theme
 D. death theme

<u>**A**</u>
<small>TE p. 371</small>

12. Shakespeare indicates that Mercutio and Tybalt both died because

 A. of their own actions.
 B. of fate.
 C. others encouraged them to fight.
 D. they were eager to prove themselves good swordsmen.

<u>**C**</u>
<small>TE p. 448</small>

13. What is Helen Keller's purpose in "Three Days to See"?

 A. to reveal the tragedy of being blind
 B. to describe in detail things she can only imagine
 C. to encourage people to appreciate their senses
 D. to express gratitude to Anne Sullivan for being her "eyes"

<u>**D**</u>
<small>pp. 27, 457</small>

14. Chesterton's use of the words "primal twilight of the first toil" in "A Piece of Chalk" shows

 A. assonance, consonance, and onomatopoeia.
 B. consonance, onomatopoeia, and alliteration.
 C. assonance, alliteration, and onomatopoeia.
 D. assonance, alliteration, and consonance.

Short Answer

Write the word or phrase that best answers the question or defines the term.

15. What does the term *genre* mean? *a common type of literature, p. 182*

16. What do both the biography and the autobiography use to tell about an incident in a person's life? *an anecdote, p. 189*

17. According to "Verifying One's References," what is Kipling's philosophy about believing what one hears? *Everything should be checked before it is believed. p. 213*

18. What allusion does Hayman use in "Sir Francis Drake" in reference to character traits being passed on? *a Biblical allusion to Elijah, p. 223*

19. What are the two modern prose fiction genres? *novel and short story, p. 226*

20. Name one incorrect conclusion Holmes draws in "The Speckled Band." *that the reference to a "band" was about the gypsies; that the metallic clang was the shutter lock dropping into place (either answer), pp. 255, 263*

21. Which kind of conflict, external or internal, is foremost in "The Drummer Boy of Shiloh"? *internal, TE p. 265*

22. What are the two major symbols that Bradbury uses throughout the story "The Drummer Boy of Shiloh," and what do they represent? *the drum and the peach blossom (youth, innocence, and/or defenselessness), pp. 265-66, 268, TE pp. 266, 269*

23. Define *fiction*. *an imagined story, p. 226*

24. Define *dramatic irony*. *situation in which a character (not the reader) is surprised at the outcome, p. 227*

25. Define *external conflict*. *a struggle that takes place outside of the protagonist, p. 227*

26. Define *internal conflict*. *a struggle within the protagonist; man against himself, p. 227*

27. Define *flat character*. *a character who has little individuality, p. 228*

28. Define *developing character*. *a character who matures and changes, p. 228*

29. Define *round character*. *a character presented in great detail, p. 228*

30. Define *static character*. *a character who remains the same throughout a work, p. 228*

31. List three characteristics of lyric poetry. *emotion, poet gives his own thoughts, personal experience,*

    p. 296

32. List at least one way in which a lyric poem is similar to a soliloquy. *(Accept any one of the*

    following ideas.) In a soliloquy and in lyric poetry, the author gives his own thoughts to an audience.

    Just as an actor gives a speech on the stage, the author gives his "speech" in a poem to his audience,

    the reader. The actor speaks of personal experience, and so does the writer of the poem. The lyric

    poem also has props, costumes, and scenery as a drama does, but in the case of the poem, these

    items are in the audience's imagination. p. 296

33. In "The Wise Old Apple Tree in Spring," what does the apple tree represent? *the beauty in life*

    that, though it does not produce anything useful, is good in and of itself; p. 308

34. Does Shakespeare show Romeo and Juliet in a respectable relationship? *yes, pp. 318-19*

35. What is ironic about Mercutio's accusing Benvolio of being quick tempered (Act III)? *Mercutio*

    himself is the one who is quick tempered. TE p. 371

36. What is ironic about Romeo's efforts to stop the fighting between Tybalt and Mercutio in Act III?

    In Romeo's effort to be peaceful, his friend ends up being killed. p. 375

37. How is the personal essay similar to a letter? *The style of the personal essay is relaxed. The essay*

    is addressed to an individual—the reader. The writer takes the reader into his confidence. He shares

    his personal experiences and thoughts with the reader. p. 436

38. What are two purposes of the personal essay? *to entertain and to teach, p. 436*

39. What is ironic about the title of Benchley's essay "How to Get Things Done"? *He actually*

    accomplishes very little of any importance. pp. 149, 450-52.

40. In "A Piece of Chalk," Chesterton compares the color white to several aspects of Christianity.
    What are two of these aspects? *virtue, mercy, chastity (any two), p. 458*

FINAL

Matching I

Match the following terms with the correct definitions.

A. anecdote	F. dramatic irony
B. autobiography	G. memoirs
C. biography	H. situational irony
D. comedy	I. tragedy
E. diary	

B
p. 188   41. interpretation of an author's own life

H
p. 149   42. a contrast between what a character expects to happen and what actually happens

F
p. 149   43. a contrast between what the reader knows and what a character in the story knows

E
p. 188   44. personal record of the events in someone's life

I
p. 184   45. play that ends unhappily

G
p. 188   46. a recollection of events from the author's public life

D
p. 185   47. play that ends happily

C
p. 188   48. history of a person's life

A
p. 189   49. a special incident from the life of an important person

Matching II

Match the following terms with the correct definitions.

A. antagonist	F. internal conflict
B. atmosphere	G. plot
C. conflict	H. protagonist
D. flashback	I. setting
E. incident	J. tone

A
p. 228   50. opponent

H
p. 228   51. main character

F
p. 227   52. man versus himself

G
p. 227   53. connected incidents

I
p. 228   54. time and place

E
p. 226   55. basic unit of a story

B
p. 228   56. the prevalent emotion of a story

J
p. 228   57. the author's attitude toward a character or situation

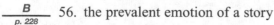

___D___ 58. summary of previous events
<small>pp. 226-27</small>

___C___ 59. contending forces
<small>p. 227</small>

Matching III

Match each work with its theme or central idea.

A. "Barbara Frietchie" 　　　E. "Lady Clare"
B. "The Drummer Boy of Shiloh"　F. "The Listeners"
C. "Foul Shot"　　　　　　　G. "The Sire de Maletroit's Door"
D. "A Gray Sleeve"　　　　　H. "Tony Kytes, the Arch-Deceiver"

___C___ 60. The author builds suspense by withholding the climax until the very end.
<small>p. 293</small>

___H___ 61. An indecisive youth is swayed by feminine charm.
<small>pp. 283-89</small>

___F___ 62. Man cannot find truth in this world.
<small>TE p. 291</small>

___D___ 63. Vague hints can mislead someone.
<small>pp. 270-79</small>

___E___ 64. True love is tested.
<small>pp. 245-47</small>

___B___ 65. An older man inspires a youth who has an inner struggle.
<small>pp. 265-68</small>

___A___ 66. A woman is ready to die for what she believes.
<small>p. 281</small>

___G___ 67. Romantic emotional incidents control the action.
<small>pp. 230-44</small>

Matching IV

Match the following imaginative comparisons with the correct examples. Answers may be used more than once or not at all.

A. metaphor
B. metonymy
C. personification
D. simile
E. synecdoche

___C___ 68. "How spring . . . defeats the orchard men of time."
<small>pp. 4, 308</small>

___A___ 69. "coil of cloisonné"
<small>pp. 4, 297</small>

___E___ 70. "Has given my heart / A change of mood"
<small>pp. 4, 312</small>

___C___ 71. "I could hear the wilderness listen."
<small>pp. 4, 310</small>

___A___ 72. "He is a brittle, crazy glass"
<small>pp. 4, 305</small>

___D___ 73. "scrolling inward like a hive"
<small>pp. 4, 297</small>

Matching V

Match each selection with its theme or central idea.

A. "Dust of Snow"	E. "Traveling Through the Dark"
B. "High Flight"	F. "Who Has Seen the Wind?"
C. "March for a One-Man Band"	G. "The Windows"
D. "Rattlesnake"	H. "The Wise Old Apple Tree in Spring"

F *pp. 301-2, TE p. 303* 74. One's inability to see something does not mean that the thing does not exist.

H *pp. 308-9, TE p. 309* 75. The beauty of something is as important as practical use.

B *pp. 306-7, TE p. 307* 76. Nature reflects the glory of "the face of God."

D *p. 297* 77. This poem gives the poet's image of and response to an animal.

C *p. 299, TE p. 300* 78. This poem emphasizes sound and syntax over rhyme.

E *p. 310, TE p. 310* 79. The speaker confronts a moral problem.

A *p. 312, TE pp. 312-13* 80. The beauty of nature may encourage someone to make the best of a situation.

G *p. 305, TE pp. 304-5* 81. This metaphoric poem compares a preacher to an inanimate object.

Matching VI

Match the following terms with the best examples from *Romeo and Juliet*.

A. alliteration	F. oxymoron
B. Biblical allusion	G. simile
C. classical allusion	H. synecdoche
D. foreshadowing	I. personification
E. metaphor	

D *pp. 151, 393* 82. "Methinks I see thee now, thou art so low, / As one dead in the bottom of a tomb."

H *pp. 4, 333* 83. "Let two more summers wither. . . ."

I *pp. 4, 333* 84. "Earth hath swallowed up all my hopes but she."

E *pp. 4, 331* 85. "Love is a smoke."

B *pp. 92, 330* 86. ". . . of nothing first created!"

A *pp. 27, 424* 87. "madman's mercy"

G *pp. 4, 344* 88. Juliet is "As a rich jewel in an Ethiop's ear."

F *p. 330, TE pp. 324, 330* 89. "Feather of lead, bright smoke, cold fire, sick health"

C *pp. 92, 359* 90. "Titan's fiery wheels"

Matching VII

Match the following terms with the correct examples of the terms.

A. alliteration F. metaphor
B. allusion G. onomatopoeia
C. assonance H. personification
D. consonance I. simile
E. irony J. symbol

_G_ 91. "I smack the pavement . . ."
p. 438

_I_ 92. "The lifting of the whole land was like the lifting of one enormous wave to wash them
p. 458 all away."

_A_ 93. "I *s*tared *s*tupidly *r*ound, *r*acking my brain for expedients."
p. 459

_D_ 94. "bearing nail*s*, bracket*s*, the evening paper*s*, and some cracker*s*"
p. 452

_H_ 95. "Silence would teach him the joys of sound."
p. 441

_J_ 96. "I suppose every one must have reflected how primeval and how poetical are the things
p. 457 that one carries in one's pocket."

_C_ 97. "peat streams of the North"
p. 457

_B_ 98. "This, I think, is the mistake that people make about old poets who lived before
p. 458 Wordsworth."

_E_ 99. "A great many people have come up to me and asked me how I manage to get so much
p. 450 work done and still keep looking so dissipated."

_F_ 100. "The narrators are usually pretty good, but there are rotten apples in every barrel."
p. 454